Glencoe Science

Biology

D1217731

Unit 6 Resources
Plants

Mc Graw Hill **Glencoe**

New York, New York   Columbus, Ohio   Chicago, Illinois   Peoria, Illinois   Woodland Hills, California

A GLENCOE PROGRAM
BIOLOGY

 biologygmh.com

Check out the following features on your **Online Learning Center:**

Study Tools

- Interactive Tables
- Interactive Time Line
- Animated illustrations
- National Geographic Visualizing animations

Self-Check Quizzes

Chapter Tests

Standardized Test Practice

Vocabulary PuzzleMaker

Interactive Tutor

Multilingual Science Glossary

Study to Go

Online Student Edition

Extensions

Virtual Labs

Microscopy Links

Periodic Table Links

Career Links

Web Links

WebQuest Projects

Science Fair Ideas

Internet BioLabs

For Teachers

Teacher Forum

Teaching Today, and much more!

Glencoe

The **McGraw·Hill** Companies

Send all inquiries to:
Glencoe/McGraw-Hill
8787 Orion Place
Columbus, OH 43240-4027

ISBN 13: 978-0-07-874610-9
ISBN 10: 0-07-874610-8

Printed in the United States of America

4 5 6 7 8 9 10   MAL   11 10 09

Table of Contents

Unit 6 Plants

Reproducible Student Pages

Teacher Guide and Answers

To the Teacher

This unit-based booklet contains resource materials to help you teach this unit more effectively. You will find the following in the chapters:

Reproducible Pages

Hands-on Activities

Launch Lab, MiniLab, and BioLab Worksheets: Each activity in this book is an expanded version of each lab that appears in the Student Edition of *Glencoe Biology*. All materials lists, procedures, and questions are repeated so that students can read and complete a lab in most cases without having a textbook on the lab table. All lab questions are reprinted with lines on which students can write their answers. In addition, for student safety, all appropriate safety symbols and caution statements have been reproduced on these expanded pages. Answer pages for each Launch Lab, MiniLab, and BioLab are included in the *Teacher Guide and Answers* section at the back of this book.

Real-World Biology: These two-page activities provide students with the opportunity to explore a technological or everyday application of biology. There are two types of Real-World Biology pages: Lab activities and Analysis activities. Each activity is directly related to a major concept in the Student Edition, and several examine principles from the physical sciences that underlie the biology content. While some activities are more hands-on, all require critical thinking and creativity. The teaching notes in the *Teacher Guide and Answers* section at the back of this book suggest chapters and topics with which to correlate the activities, explain the purpose of each activity, present career applications for the relevant field of science, offer materials tips and safety tips for the Lab activities, provide teaching strategies that include ideas for below-level and above-level students, and give answers to all questions on the student pages.

Extension and Intervention

Diagnostic Test: Each Diagnostic Test provides an opportunity for students to predict answers to questions about the chapter content based on what they already know. The students decide on one of the possible answers given, and then explain their reasoning. Answers to the questions and explanations for student preconceptions are given in the *Teacher Guide and Answers* section. These student predictions to the questions will allow you to design your lessons to meet the students' needs.

Enrichment: *Enrichment* pages offer research activities to students who need additional challenges. There are three types of *Enrichment* activities: Diagramming, Analyze a Problem, and Group Project. Diagramming activities have students use resources to draw and label their own diagrams. Analyze a Problem activities have students research, discuss, and write about specific topics. Group Project activities have students work in groups to research topics, organize information, and make class presentations.

To the Teacher continued

Concept Mapping: The *Concept Mapping* worksheets reinforce and extend the graphic organizational skills introduced in the Skill Handbook in the Student Edition. Concept maps are visual representations of relationships among particular concepts. By using these worksheets, students will gain experience with six different types of concept maps: the network tree, which shows causal information, group hierarchies, and branching procedures; the flowchart, which is similar to an events chain but has more possibilities for events; the cycle map, which shows a series of events without a final outcome; the Venn diagram, which illustrates similarities and differences between items; the events chain, which describes the stages of a process, the steps in a linear procedure, or a sequence of events; and the cycle map, which shows how a series of events interacts to produce a set of results again and again.

There is one *Concept Mapping* worksheet for each chapter in the Student Edition. Each worksheet is geared toward a specific section or sections in the chapter so that you can assign it at the most relevant time. An entire section or just a few key concepts from the section might be mapped. Answers to all *Concept Mapping* worksheets are provided in the *Teacher Guide and Answers* section at the back of this book.

Study Guide in English and Spanish: These pages help students understand, organize, and compare the main biology concepts in the textbook. The questions and activities also help build strong study and reading skills. There are four study guide pages for each chapter. Students will find these pages easy to follow because the section titles match those in the textbook. Italicized sentences in the study guide direct students to the related topics in the text.

The *Study Guide* exercises employ a variety of formats including multiple-choice, matching, true/false, ordering, labeling, completion, and short answer questions. The clear, easy-to-follow exercises and the self-pacing format are geared to build your students' confidence in understanding biology. The English pages are followed immediately by the study guide pages in Spanish.

Section Quick Check: The *Section Quick Check* pages provide students an overview of the text using a short-answer format. Each page of questions is correlated to a section of the Student Edition, and the items are different from those in the Student Edition for broader coverage of section content. The questions utilize Bloom's verbs and are scaffolded according to difficulty from easiest to hardest.

Chapter Tests: The Chapter Tests are arranged in five parts with five different types of questions. These worksheets provide materials to assess your students understanding of concepts from each chapter in the unit.

- Test A (below level): Multiple Choice, Matching, Interpreting, Short Answer, and Concept Application

- Test B (on level): Multiple Choice, Matching and Completion, Interpreting, Short Answer, and Concept Application

- Test C (above level): Multiple Choice, Matching and Completion, Interpreting, Short Answer, and Concept Application

The *Multiple Choice, Matching,* and *Completion* questions test comprehension of the vocabulary of the chapter.

The *Interpreting* questions ask the student to combine factual and explanatory information. Students will need to interpret data and discover relationships presented in graphs, tables, and diagrams.

The *Short Answer* questions allow the student to express understanding of the information. Students will apply their understanding of concepts to solve problems, compare and contrast situations, make inferences or predictions, and explain their reasoning.

The *Concept Application* questions present the student with a situation. These situations give the student the opportunity to demonstrate both reasoning and creative skills.

Student Recording Sheet: Student Recording Sheets allow students to use the Chapter Assessment and the Standardized Test Practice questions in the Student Edition as a practice for standardized tests. Student Recording Sheets give them the opportunity to use bubble answer grids and numbers grids for recording answers. Answers for the Student Recording Sheets can be found in the Teacher Wraparound Edition on *Chapter Assessment* and *Standardized Test Practice* pages.

Teacher Guide and Answers: Answers or possible answers for questions in this booklet can be found in the *Teacher Guide and Answers* section. Materials, teaching strategies, and content background, along with chapter references, are also provided where appropriate.

Student Lab Safety Form

Student Name: _____

Date: _____

Lab Title: _____

In order to show your teacher that you understand the safety concerns of this lab, the following questions must be answered after the teacher explains the information to you. You must have your teacher initial this form before you can proceed with the lab.

1. How would you describe what you will be doing during this lab?

2. What are the safety concerns associated with this lab (as explained by your teacher)?

- _____
- _____
- _____
- _____
- _____

3. What additional safety concerns or questions do you have?

Table of Contents

Chapter 21 Introduction to Plants

Diagnostic Test

CHAPTER 21

Introduction to Plants

Before reading Chapter 21, predict answers to questions about the chapter content based on what you already know. Circle the letter of the correct answer, and then explain your reasoning.

1. While walking around a pond at a park, Danielle observes aquatic plants such as water hyacinth and water lilies floating on the surface of the water. She wonders how a tall, land plant such as an oak tree gets water to its leaves and decides to research her question. Which explanation does she research?

   A. Oak tree leaves take in water vapor from the air.

   B. Tree leaves absorb rainwater through leaf pores.

   C. Tube-like tissues transport water through the trunk.

   D. Water moves up the trunk by osmosis or diffusion.

   Explain.

   _____

   _____

   _____

2. John and several of his friends are backpacking in the Adirondack Mountains. At a local ranger station, a display explains the basic taxonomy of plants they might see during their trip. Which statement would John read on the display?

   A. Flowering plants are classified into several divisions in Kingdom Plantae.

   B. Kingdom Plantae is divided into several major groups called phyla.

   C. Simple plants, such as mosses and ferns, are classified in the same phylum.

   D. Spruce, fir, and pine trees are classified in Division Coniferophyta.

   Explain.

   _____

   _____

   _____

3. Tammy is attending a garden lecture, and she learns about annual, biennial, and perennial plants. List several characteristics she learns about these plants during the lecture.

   _____

   _____

   _____

Launch **Lab**

CHAPTER 21
What characteristics differ among plants?

Scientists use specific characteristics to group plants within the plant kingdom. In this lab, you will examine some of the characteristics of plants.

Procedure 🔍 👕 ☣️ 🧤

1. Read and complete the lab safety form.
2. Label **five plant specimens** using letters *A*, *B*, *C*, *D*, and *E*.
3. Study each plant carefully. Wash your hands thoroughly after handling plant material.

4. Based on your observations, list characteristics that describe the differences and similarities among these plants.
5. Rank your list of characteristics based on what you consider the most and least important.

Data and Observations

Analysis

1. **Compare** your list to your classmates' lists.

_____

_____

2. **Describe** the diversity among the plants you studied.

_____

_____

_____

3. **List** plant characteristics that you could not observe that might be useful in organizing these plants into groups.

_____

_____

_____

MiniLab

Compare Plant Cuticles

Does the cuticle vary among different types of plants? Plant leaves are covered with a cuticle that reduces water loss. The thickness of cuticle material varies among plants.

Procedure

1. Read and complete the lab safety form.
2. Write a description of each **leaf** type provided by your teacher.
3. Pile each type of leaf on separate but identical **plastic plates.** Measure the mass and then adjust the amount of leaves on each plate until they are of equal mass. Record the masses.
4. The next day, examine each plate of leaves. Record your observations.
5. Measure the mass of each plate of leaves and record the data.

Data and Observations

Analysis

1. **Interpret Data** Which leaves appeared to have lost more water? Do the data support your observation?

_____

_____

2. **Infer** which leaves might have more cuticle.

_____

_____

MiniLab

CHAPTER 21

Investigate Conifer Leaves

What similarities and differences exist among conifer leaves? Some conifer trees are among the tallest and oldest organisms on Earth. Most conifers have needlelike leaves that differ in a variety of ways. Leaf characteristics are important in conifer identification.

Procedure

1. Read and complete the lab safety form.
2. Obtain one of each of the **conifer samples** your teacher has identified. Label each sample by name.
3. Design a data table to record your observations.
4. Compare and contrast the leaves. Make a list of characteristics that you determine are important for describing each sample. Record these characteristics for each conifer sample.

5. Develop a system for grouping the conifer samples. Be prepared to justify your system.
6. Wash your hands thoroughly after handling plant samples.

Data and Observations

Analysis

1. **Explain** the reasoning for your classification system.

_____

_____

_____

2. **Compare** your classification system to those created by other students. Explain why your system is an efficient way to classify the conifer samples that you studied.

_____

_____

_____

BioLab

Field Investigation: How can you identify and classify trees?

Background: Botanists and others interested in plants often use field guides and dichotomous keys to identify plants. In this BioLab, you will use a field guide to identify trees in a given area. Then, you will create your own dichotomous key to identify the trees in your area.

Question: *What characteristics can be used to identify trees and to create a dichotomous key for them?*

Materials
field guide of trees (for your area)
metric ruler
magnifying lens

Safety Precautions
WARNING: *Stay within the area of study and be alert for plants, insects, or other organisms that might pose a hazard.*

Procedure
1. Read and complete the lab safety form.
2. Study the field guide provided by your teacher to determine how it is organized.
3. Based on your examination of the field guide and what you learned about plant characteristics in this chapter, make a list of characteristics that will help you identify the trees in your area.
4. Create a data table based on the list you made in step 3.
5. Use a field guide to identify a tree in the area designated by your teacher. Confirm your identification with your teacher.
6. Record in your data table the characteristics of your identified tree.
7. Repeat steps 5 and 6 until you have identified all trees required for this lab.
8. Review your data table. Choose the characteristics most helpful in identifying trees. These characteristics will form the basis of your dichotomous key.
9. Determine in what rank the characteristics should appear in the dichotomous key. Create a written description for each characteristic.
10. Create your dichotomous key. The traits described at each step of a dichotomous key are usually pairs of contrasting characteristics. For example, the first step might compare needlelike or scalelike leaves to broad leaves.

Data and Observations

Analyze and Conclude

1. **Interpret Data** Based on the data you collected, describe plant diversity in the area you studied.

_____

_____

_____

2. **Critique** Exchange your dichotomous key for a classmate's dichotomous key. Use the key to identify trees in the study area. Give your classmate suggestions to improve his or her key.

3. **Predict** How effective would your dichotomous key be for someone trying to identify trees in the study area? Explain.

_____

_____

_____

4. **Error Analysis** What changes could you make to improve the effectiveness of your dichotomous key?

_____

_____

_____

Real-World Biology: Analysis

Plants for Gardens and Landscapes

Scientists classify plants into 12 divisions, based on the characteristics of the plants and how closely related the plants are. The plants in each division are further divided into smaller groups of related plants. Each individual type of plant is given a scientific name that is made up of the genus it belongs to and the species it is. For example, the scientific name of a sunflower is *Helianthus annuus*. *Helianthus* is the genus in which a sunflower belongs. A sunflower's species name is *annuus*. Other plant species that are related to sunflowers also belong to the genus *Helianthus*.

Using scientific names for plants ensures that everyone is talking about the same plant. But what if a person who is not a scientist and not an avid gardener wants to choose plants for a garden or landscape? Knowing a plant's scientific name doesn't help the average person know what environmental conditions the plant needs or what characteristics the plant has. In this activity, you will examine other ways plants can be grouped.

Part A: Other Ways to Group Plants

Grouping plants in other ways is useful to gardeners and landscapers. Catalogs, plant nurseries, and garden stores often group plants by their characteristics. This information helps people choose plants that they like and that will grow well where planted. **Table 1** lists some of the questions a person buying plants might ask and possible answers to the questions. Study the table and then answer the Analyze and Conclude questions.

Table 1

Questions	Possible Answers
What do I want to plant?	flower, vegetable, deciduous tree or shrub, evergreen tree or shrub, vine, groundcover
How long is the plant's life span?	annual, biennial, perennial
How much sunlight does the plant need?	• full sunlight (at least 6 hours) • partial shade (3–4 hours) • shade (bright reflected light but little or no direct sunlight)
How much moisture does the plant need?	• will grow in dry soil • grows best in moist places
How big will the plant grow?	• height and width of mature plant • size of flower, fruit, vegetable, or leaves

Analyze and Conclude

Respond to each statement.

1. **State** what a person needs to know before buying plants.

_____

_____

_____

_____

_____

2. Suppose you were choosing plants for an area with large trees. **Determine** what main factor you would need to consider.

_____

_____

_____

Part B: Cultivars and Varieties

Catalogs, plant nurseries, and garden centers provide a wealth of information about plants. Of course, one of the main pieces of information is the names of the plants. Sometimes, only the common names are used. Often, both the common names and scientific names are used. But what would you think if the common name of a plant was Black-eyed Susan, and its scientific name was *R. hirta* 'Prairie Sun' instead of *Rudbeckia hirta?* The first part is easy. The genus name *Rudbeckia* is abbreviated. 'Prairie Sun' in single quotes is added to the scientific name and is the name of the cultivar. A cultivar is a group of plants that has been developed from a species and maintained by cultivation of specific characteristics. It does not exist in nature. The word *cultivar* comes from the words *cultivated* and *variety.*

Variety is another term that is added to the scientific name of some plants. These plants are subspecies of a natural species. The subspecies are different enough to have separate names, but not different enough to be separate species. Cabbage is *Brassica olerocea capitata,* and broccoli is *Brassica oleracea italica.* Notice that the variety names—*capitata* and *italica*—are Latin and written in italic. Study the plant names in **Table 2** and then answer the questions.

Table 2

	Common Name	Scientific Name
Plant 1	coneflower	*Echinacea purpurea*
Plant 2	coneflower	*Echinacea purpurea* 'Fragrant Angel'
Plant 3	cauliflower	*Brassica oleracea botrytis*

Analyze and Conclude

*Use **Table 2** to respond to each question and statement.*

1. **Identify** which of the three plants above is a cultivar. How do you know?

_____

_____

2. **Explain** what each word means in the scientific name for Plant 3. Use the terms *species, variety,* and *genus* in your answer.

_____

_____

_____

3. **Contrast** What is the difference between a cultivar and a variety?

_____

_____

_____

_____

CAREERS IN BIOLOGY

Horticulture Visit biologygmh.com for information on horticulturists. What are the responsibilities of a horticulturist?

Enrichment

Group Project: Plant Classification and Use

Plants are grouped as either nonvascular or vascular. The vascular plants are further grouped into plants without seeds and those with seeds. The nonvascular plants include the following divisions: Bryophyta, Hepaticophyta, and Anthocerotophyta. The divisions of the seedless vascular plants include Pterophyta, Psilotophyta, Sphenophyta, and Lycophyta. To most people, the most familiar plants are the vascular seed plants. These include the divisions Cycadophyta, Ginkgophyta, Gnetophyta, Coniferophyta, and Anthophyta. Plants have many uses. For example, we use plants as food and medicine and to make paper, fabric, and building materials. Some plants are prized for their beauty or fragrance.

Select Working in a small group, select one of the plants listed in the table to research. For example, one group might research the California redwood, while another group researches the prickly pear cactus.

Research Once you have selected a plant, use your textbook and other reference materials to find information. Fill in the classification table below for the plant you selected. Your research should also include information on the plant's habitat and uses of the plant. Look for photographs of the plant.

Present Finally, present the information that you researched about the plant to your class. Show any photographs of the plant that you found. As other groups give their presentations, complete the table. After all the groups have given their presentations, have a class discussion to address everyone's questions.

Common Name	Nonvascular/ Vascular	Division	Scientific Name
Common liverwort			
California redwood			
Mormon tea			
Peat moss			
Ponderosa pine			
Prickly pear cactus			
Purple coneflower			
Western bracken fern			
White willow			

Concept Mapping

Classification of Plants

Complete the network tree about the classification of plants. These terms may be used more than once: anthophytes, bryophytes, cones, conifers, ferns, horsetails, liverworts, mosses, nonvascular plants, seeds, vascular plants.

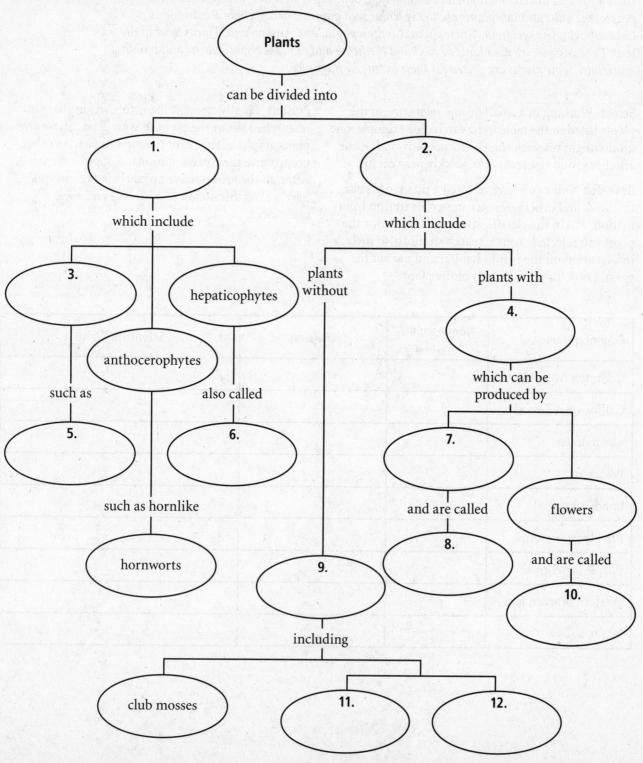

Study Guide

CHAPTER 21

Section 1: Plant Evolution and Adaptations

In your textbook, read about plant evolution.

Complete the table by checking the correct column(s) for each characteristic.

Characteristic	Green Algae	Plants
1. Cell walls composed of cellulose		
2. Stomata to enable the exchange of gases		
3. Cell division that includes formation of a cell plate		
4. Chlorophyll for photosynthesis		
5. Waxy cuticle to retain water		
6. Vascular tissue to transport substances		
7. Food stored as starch		

In your textbook, read about plant adaptations to land environments.

Respond to the following statement.

Name five adaptations to a land environment that plants have developed.

8. _____

9. _____

10. _____

11. _____

12. _____

In your textbook, read about the alternation of generations

Use each of the terms below only once to complete the passage.

| diploid | dominant | gametophyte | haploid | spores | sporophyte |

An alternation of generations for plants includes a **(13)** _____ gametophyte

generation and a **(14)** _____ sporophyte generation.

The **(15)** _____ generation produces eggs and sperm, which unite to

form a **(16)** _____ . This new generation, which is generally the more

(17) _____ generation, produces **(18)** _____ that

can become the next gametophyte generation.

Study Guide

CHAPTER 21

Section 2: Nonvascular Plants

In your textbook, read about the diversity of nonvascular plants.

Refer to the illustration of bryophytes and hepaticophytes. Use each of the terms below only once to complete the passage.

Bryophyta	climates	**Hepaticophyta**	leaves
multicellular rhizoids	primitive	**thallose**	unicellular rhizoids

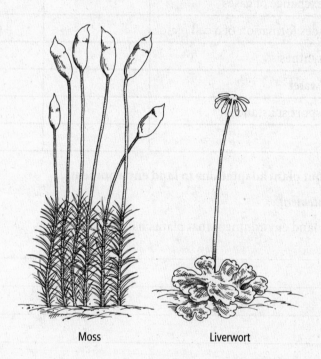

Moss   Liverwort

A moss is in the division (**1**) _____ . A liverwort is in the division

(**2**) _____ . Mosses have rootlike (**3**) _____

that anchor them to the soil, and liverworts have (**4**) _____ . Both mosses

and liverworts have structures that are similar to (**5**) _____ . Both can

grow in a variety of (**6**) _____ . Liverworts are the most

(**7**) _____ of land plants. Liverworts are classified as either

(**8**) _____ or leafy.

Study Guide

Section 3: Seedless Vascular Plants

In your textbook, read about the diversity of seedless vascular plants.

Complete the table by checking the correct column(s) for each description.

Description	Lycophyta	Pterophyta
1. Do not produce seeds		
2. Include club or spike mosses		
3. Include ferns and horsetails		
4. Have a cluster of spore-bearing structures called the strobilus		
5. Have fronds with branched vascular tissue		
6. Use a rhizome for food storage		
7. Resemble small pine trees		

In your textbook, read about division Lycophyta and division Pterophyta.

If the statement is true, write true. *If the statement is false, replace the italicized word or phrase to make it true.*

8. Some *lycophytes* live anchored to an object or another plant.

_____

9. Ferns grow *only in wet areas*.

_____

10. Both lycophytes and pterophytes produce *spores*.

_____

11. The dominant generation of lycophytes is the *gametophyte*.

_____

12. Fern spores form in a *sporangium*.

_____

13. Fern *sporophytes* are tiny.

_____

14. The *strobili* of lycophytes are shaped like clubs or spikes.

_____

Study Guide

Section 4: Vascular Seed Plants

In your textbook, read about the diversity of seed plants.

Complete the table by writing an example and a description for each division.

Division	Example and Description
Cycadophyta	1. _____ _____ _____ _____
Gnetophyta	2. _____ _____ _____
Ginkgophyta	3. _____ _____ _____ _____
Coniferophyta	4. _____ _____ _____ _____
Anthophyta	5. _____ _____ _____ _____

Guía de estudio

Sección 1: La evolución y las adaptaciones de las plantas

En tu libro de texto, lee acerca de la evolución de las plantas.

Completa la tabla marcando la(s) columna(s) correcta(s) para cada característica.

Característica	Alga verde	Plantas
1. Paredes celulares compuestas de celulosa		
2. La estomata que permite el intercambio de gases		
3. División celular que incluye la formación de una placa celular		
4. Clorofila para la fotosíntesis		
5. Cutícula cerosa para retener el agua		
6. Tejido vascular para transportar substancias		
7. Alimento almacenado en la forma de almidón		

En tu libro de texto, lee acerca de las adaptaciones de las plantas a los ambientes terrestres.

Responde a la siguiente afirmación.

Enumera cinco adaptaciones a un ambiente terrestre que las plantas han desarrollado.

8. _____

9. _____

10. _____

11. _____

12. _____

En tu libro de texto, lee acerca de la alternación de generaciones.

Usa cada uno de los siguientes términos sólo una vez para completar el párrafo.

diploides   dominante   esporas   esporofito   gametofito   haploides

Una alternación de generaciones para las plantas incluye una generación de gametofitos

(13) _____ y una generación de esporofitos

(14) _____ . La generación de (15) _____

produce huevos y esperma, los cuales se unen para formar un (16) _____ .

Esta nueva generación, la cual es generalmente la generación más (17) _____ ,

produce (18) _____ que se pueden convertir en la siguiente generación

de gametofitos.

Guía de estudio

En tu libro de texto, lee acerca de la diversidad de las plantas no vasculares.

Consulta la ilustración de briofitas y hepaticopsidas. Usa cada uno de los términos a continuación sólo una vez para completar el párrafo.

Bryophyta	**climas**	**Hepaticopsida**	**hojas**
primitivas	**rizoides multicelulares**	**rizoides unicelulares**	**talosas**

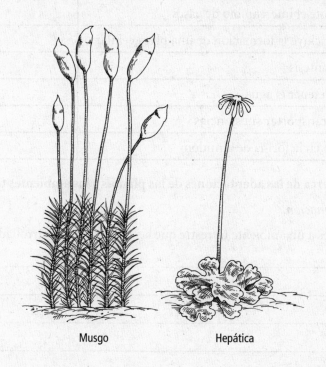

Musgo   Hepática

Un musgo pertenece a la división (**1**) _____ . Una hepática

pertenece a la división (**2**) _____ . Los musgos tienen

(**3**) _____ como raíces que se pegan al suelo, y las hepáticas tienen

(**4**) _____ . Tanto los musgos como las hepáticas tienen estructuras que son

similares a las (**5**) _____ . Ambas pueden crecer en una variedad

de (**6**) _____ . Las hepáticas son las más (**7**) _____

de las plantas terrestres. Las hepáticas se clasifican como (**8**) _____ o frondosas.

Guía de estudio

En tu libro de texto, lee acerca de la diversidad de las plantas vasculares sin semilla.

Completa la tabla marcando la(s) columna(s) correcta(s) para cada descripción.

Descripción	Licofitas	Terofitas
1. No producen semillas.		
2. Incluyen los musgos de palo o púas.		
3. Incluyen helechos y colas de caballo.		
4. Tienen un conjunto de estructuras con esporas llamadas estróbilos.		
5. Tienen frondas con tejido vascular ramificado.		
6. Usan un rizoma para almacenar alimento.		
7. Se asemejan a pequeños pinos.		

En tu libro de texto, lee acerca de la división de las licofitas y la división de las terofitas.

Si la afirmación es verdadera, escribe «verdadero». Si la afirmación es falsa, sustituye la palabra o frase en cursiva para volverla verdadera.

8. Algunas *licofitas* viven ancladas a un objeto u otra planta.

_____

9. Los helechos crecen *únicamente en áreas húmedas*.

_____

10. Tanto las licofitas como las terofitas producen *esporas*.

_____

11. La generación dominante de licofitas es el *gametofito*.

_____

12. Las esporas de los helechos forman un *esporangio*.

_____

13. Los *esporofitos* de los helechos son pequeños.

_____

14. Los *estróbilos* de las licofitas tienen forma de palo o púas.

_____

Guía de estudio

Sección 4: Plantas vasculares con semilla

En tu libro de texto, lee acerca de la diversidad de las plantas con semilla.

Completa la tabla con un ejemplo y una descripción para cada división.

División	Ejemplo y descripción
Cicadofitas	1. _____ _____ _____ _____
Gnetofitas	2. _____ _____ _____ _____
Ginkgofitas	3. _____ _____ _____ _____
Coniferofitas	4. _____ _____ _____ _____
Antofitas	5. _____ _____ _____ _____

Section Quick Check

Section 1: Plant Evolution and Adaptations

After reading the section in your textbook, respond to each statement.

1. List the two groups that the 12 plant divisions can be divided into.

_____

2. Review the common characteristics of green algae and plants.

_____

_____

_____

_____

3. Indicate a reason why vascular plants can grow taller than nonvascular plants, besides the fact that vascular tissue provides support.

_____

_____

_____

_____

4. Classify A plant has specialized transport systems and is tall. It reproduces with spores. Determine if it is a nonvascular plant, a seedless vascular plant, or a vascular plant with seeds. Explain.

_____

_____

_____

_____

5. Infer why plants that live in deserts have thick cuticles. Explain.

_____

_____

_____

Section
Quick Check

CHAPTER 21
Section 2: Nonvascular Plants

After reading the section in your textbook, respond to each statement.

1. **Name** the three divisions of nonvascular plants. **Cite** examples of each.

   _____

   _____

2. **Recall** the purpose of mucilage in the spaces around the cells of hornworts.

   _____

   _____

3. **Compare** and **contrast** liverworts and mosses.

   _____

   _____

   _____

   _____

4. **Determine** which of the nonvascular plants are most like vascular plants. Explain.

   _____

   _____

   _____

5. **Infer** why liverworts often grow close to the ground and in areas with plenty of moisture.

   _____

   _____

   _____

Section Quick Check

Section 3: Seedless Vascular Plants

After reading the section in your textbook, respond to each statement.

1. **Define** *epiphyte*.

_____

_____

2. **Describe** the life cycle of a fern. Use the terms *gametophyte, spores, sporangium,* and *sporophyte* in your answer.

_____

_____

_____

3. **Compare** horsetails and lycophytes.

_____

_____

_____

4. **Theorize** why ferns that live in areas with cold winters have a rhizome.

_____

_____

_____

5. **Deduce** why ferns that live in dry areas need to be able to produce sporophytes without fertilization.

_____

_____

Section
Quick Check

CHAPTER 21
Section 4: Vascular Seed Plants

After reading the section in your textbook, respond to each statement.

1. **List** the characteristics of conifers.

_____

_____

_____

2. **Explain** what the name *gymnosperm* means and how it describes plants that are gymnosperms.

_____

_____

_____

3. **Describe** how the terms *evergreen* and *deciduous* are applied to plants in temperate and tropical climates.

_____

_____

_____

_____

_____

4. **Classify** A gardener has a plant in his garden. When winter comes, the plant drops its leaves. During spring, new leaves grow, and the plant flowers. The plant drops its leaves in the winter. New leaves grow next spring. Classify this plant by its life span and reproductive structures, and justify your answer.

_____

_____

_____

5. **Infer** the advantage of *Welwitschia* absorbing water through its leaves.

_____

_____

_____

_____

Chapter Test A

CHAPTER 21
Introduction to Plants

Part A: Multiple Choice

In the space at the left, write the letter of the term or phrase that best answers each question.

_____ **1.** Which describes a plant?
   A. multicellular eukaryote
   B. multicellular prokaryote
   C. unicellular eukaryote
   D. unicellular prokaryote

_____ **2.** Which organisms are believed to be the ancestor of land plants?
   A. algae
   B. corals
   C. rotifers
   D. sponges

_____ **3.** Which structure protects the developing embryo of a beech tree?
   A. cotyledon
   B. cuticle
   C. seed
   D. stomata

Part B: Matching

Write the letter of the correct plant division on the line next to its member. Answers may be used only once.

_____ **1.** moss   **A.** Anthophyta

_____ **2.** daisy   **B.** Bryophyta

_____ **3.** white pine tree   **C.** Coniferophyta

Part C: Interpreting Diagrams and Charts

Write your response to each statement in the space provided.

Seed Structure

1. Study the diagram on the right. **Identify** the types of seed structures labeled *A*, *B*, and *C*.

   A. _____

   B. _____

   C. _____

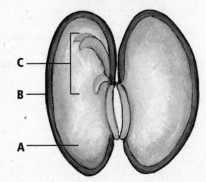

Chapter Test A CONTINUED

2. Study the evolutionary tree on the right. **Identify** the types of plants for the arrows labeled *A–C* on the chart.

A. _____

B. _____

C. _____

3. **Analyze** the evolutionary tree. **Compare** the appearance of gymnosperms in the fossil record with the appearance of angiosperms.

_____

_____

_____

_____

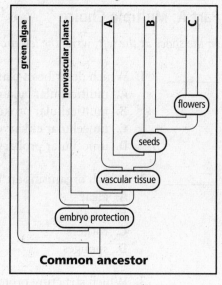

The Evolutionary Tree of Plants

green algae
nonvascular plants
A
B
C
flowers
seeds
vascular tissue
embryo protection
Common ancestor

Part D: Short Answer

Write your response to each statement in the space provided.

1. **Infer** how vascular tissues help plants survive in land environments.

_____

_____

_____

_____

2. **Contrast** the life spans of annual, biennial, and perennial plants.

_____

_____

Chapter Test A CONTINUED

Part E: Concept Application

Write your response to each statement in the space provided.

1. **Compare** Sheila observes alga cells and oak leaf cells under a microscope. Her teacher asks Sheila to research the similarities of alga cells and oak leaf cells. What comparisons does she make? Use the terms *cellulose* and *cell plate* in your discussion.

_____

_____

_____

2. Science students are conducting a survey of trees in a forest. Their teacher asks the class to describe the reproductive structures of a white pine tree. **Identify** the structures that the students will describe. **Explain** the functions of the structures.

_____

_____

_____

Chapter Test B

CHAPTER 21

Introduction to Plants

Part A: Multiple Choice

In the space at the left, write the letter of the term or phrase that best answers each question.

_____ 1. Which organism is believed to be the ancestor of oak trees?
A. multicellular, freshwater green algae
B. multicellular, marine green algae
C. unicellular, freshwater green algae
D. unicellular, marine green algae

_____ 2. Which is a vascular plant that does not produce seeds?
A. beech tree
B. hornwort
C. horsetail
D. rosebush

_____ 3. Which structure would anchor green moss to a decaying log?
A. frond
B. rhizoid
C. root
D. sorus

_____ 4. Which strategy do ferns use to survive drought?
A. closing off vascular tissues
B. dispersing dormant seeds
C. slowing down life processes
D. storing water in frond tissues

_____ 5. Which is part of the life cycle of an annual plant?
A. drops its leaves during harsh conditions
B. lives a full year before reproducing
C. requires two years to produce flowers
D. sprouts, grows, and dies in one season

Part B: Matching and Completion

Matching Set 1 *Write the letter of the correct plant division on the line next to the description of its member. Answers may be used only once or not at all.*

_____ 1. moss growing on stream rocks

A. Anthocerophyta

_____ 2. commonly called liverworts

B. Bryophyta

_____ 3. grew 30 m tall millions of years ago

C. Hepaticophyta

_____ 4. classifies ferns and horsetails

D. Lycophyta

E. Pterophyta

Chapter Test **B** CONTINUED

Matching Set 2 *Write the letter of the correct plant division on the line next to the description of its member. Answers may be used only once or not at all.*

_____ **5.** have soft trunks and resemble palm trees

_____ **6.** have fan-shaped leaves and tolerate air pollution well

_____ **7.** classifies all grass species

_____ **8.** have adaptations to survive cold climates

A. Anthophyta

B. Coniferophyta

C. Cycadophyta

D. Ginkgophyta

E. Gnetophyta

Completion *Write the correct term in the blank to complete each sentence below.*

9. An opening in the outer layer of a leaf that allows oxygen to escape is called

a(n) _____ .

10. Plant structures that quickly move water, sugar, and nutrients through a plant are

called _____ .

11. DNA analysis reveals that the most primitive type of land plant is

commonly known as a(n) _____ .

Part C: Interpreting Diagrams and Charts

Write your response to each statement in the space provided.

Seed Structure

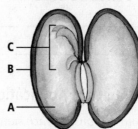

1. Study the diagram on the right. **Identify** the types of seed structures labeled *A*, *B*, and *C*. **Identify** the structure that will develop into a new plant.

A. _____

B. _____

C. _____

_____

2. Study the evolutionary tree on the right. **Identify** the types of plants for the arrows labeled *A–D* on the chart.

A. _____

B. _____

C. _____

D. _____

The Evolutionary Tree of Plants

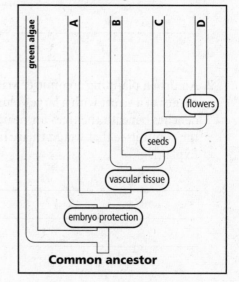

Chapter Test B CONTINUED

3. **Contrast** the placement of seeds and flowers on the evolutionary tree. **Infer** why scientists have placed these two structures on the chart in their present locations.

_____

_____

_____

Part D: Short Answer

Write your response to each statement in the space provided.

1. **Hypothesize** the effects of a chemical that breaks down the cuticle of a plant if this chemical is sprayed on the plant.

_____

_____

_____

2. **Infer** the adaptations that enable blue spruce trees to survive the cold climate of Canada. Include the term *cutin* in your answer.

_____

_____

_____

Part E: Concept Application

Write your response to each statement in the space provided.

1. **Compare** *Spirogyra* green algae and a rosebush.

_____

_____

_____

2. An urban planning committee wants to plant trees on an abandoned lot at the corner of a street with a large volume of traffic. The committee would like to place benches beneath the trees for nearby workers to rest. **Recommend** a type of tree to the committee that would thrive in this location and meet their planning objectives. Explain.

_____

_____

_____

_____

Chapter Test **C**

CHAPTER 21
Introduction to Plants

Part A: Multiple Choice

In the space at the left, write the letter of the term, phrase, or sentence that best answers each question.

_____ 1. Which feature of modern plant cells is **not** found in modern alga cells?
- **A.** cell plate
- **B.** cellulose-containing cell wall
- **C.** nuclear DNA
- **D.** ribosomal RNA

_____ 2. Which division classifies green moss growing on a stone building?
- **A.** Anthocerophyta
- **B.** Bryophyta
- **C.** Lycophyta
- **D.** Pterophyta

_____ 3. In which habitat would a botanist be most likely to find a new species of a nonvascular plant?
- **A.** cool mountain lake
- **B.** damp forest soil
- **C.** high tree branches
- **D.** sunlit sand dune

_____ 4. Which is a unique characteristic of plants classified in Division Anthocerophyta?
- **A.** have one chloroplast in each cell
- **B.** lack of photosynthesizing structures
- **C.** once used to cure liver ailments
- **D.** turns into coal after millions of years

_____ 5. Which is the reason botanists believe liverworts are the most primitive terrestrial plant?
- **A.** DNA analysis suggests liverworts diverged at an earlier time.
- **B.** Liverwort leaves contain a primitive form of stomata.
- **C.** Liverwort spores have a simplistic spore and DNA structure.
- **D.** Liverworts must rely on diffusion to transport nutrients.

_____ 6. Which is a characteristic of an annual plant?
- **A.** can have fleshy storage roots
- **B.** develops flowers in two years
- **C.** drops leaves in harsh conditions
- **D.** lives for one growing season

Part B: Completion

Write the correct term in the blank to complete each sentence below.

1. Horsetail plants are classified in Division _____ .

2. Decayed moss that can be burned in a fireplace is called _____ .

Chapter Test C CONTINUED

3. Upon reaching favorable conditions, a club-moss spore will grow to form the

_____ stage.

4. Coal burning power plants would have no fuel without fossilized ancient plants from

Division _____ .

5. A new species of plant that has vascular tissues and stores food in a rhizome would be classified

in Division _____ .

6. A food absorbing structure in a seed is called a(n) _____ .

Part C: Interpreting Diagrams and Charts

Write your response to each statement in the space provided.

Seed Structure

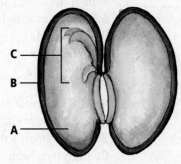

1. Study the diagram on the right. **Identify** the types
of seed structure labeled *A*, *B*, and *C*. **Infer** the function
of structure B.

A. _____

B. _____

C. _____

_____

2. Study the evolutionary tree on the right. **Identify** the types of
plants for the arrows labeled *A–E* on the chart. **Describe** how seeds advanced the
colonization of land for plants.

A. _____

B. _____

C. _____

D. _____

E. _____

_____

_____

_____

The Evolutionary Tree of Plants

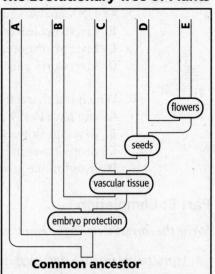

flowers

seeds

vascular tissue

embryo protection

Common ancestor

3. Infer the major event on the evolutionary tree of plants that led to
the appearance of diverse terrestrial ecosystems. Explain.

_____

_____

Chapter Test C CONTINUED

Part D: Short Answer

Write your response to each statement in the space provided.

1. **Describe** the characteristics most plants share.

   _____

   _____

   _____

2. **Discuss** four structures that are critical for the survival of terrestrial plants.

   _____

   _____

   _____

Part E: Concept Application

Write your response to each statement in the space provided.

1. A botanist is training a group of volunteers to survey the plants of a mature deciduous forest. The botanist wants to give the volunteers a lecture about the basic plant taxonomy they should know for identifying plants in this forest. **Develop** the basic points the botanist should include in the lecture.

   _____

   _____

   _____

2. Norway maple trees produce seeds surrounded by keys, which are structures that spin as they fall and drift on the wind. **Predict** the effect on a population of Norway maple trees if a new species of caterpillar is introduced that feeds on the key structure surrounding the plant's seed (but not the seed) while the keys are still on the tree.

   _____

   _____

   _____

3. **Hypothesize** why most conifer trees cannot grow in tropical rain forests.

   _____

   _____

   _____

   _____

CHAPTER 21
Assessment   Student Recording Sheet

Section 21.1

Vocabulary Review

Write the vocabulary term that best matches each phrase.

1. _____ 2. _____ 3. _____

Understand Key Concepts

Select the best answer from the choices given, and fill in the corresponding circle.

4. Ⓐ Ⓑ Ⓒ Ⓓ   5. Ⓐ Ⓑ Ⓒ Ⓓ   6. Ⓐ Ⓑ Ⓒ Ⓓ   7. Ⓐ Ⓑ Ⓒ Ⓓ

Constructed Response

8. _____
   _____
   _____

9. _____

Think Critically

10. Record your answer for question 10 on a separate sheet of paper.

Section 21.2

Vocabulary Review

Write a sentence using the vocabulary term.

11. _____
    _____

Understand Key Concepts

Select the best answer from the choices given, and fill in the corresponding circle.

12. Ⓐ Ⓑ Ⓒ Ⓓ   13. Ⓐ Ⓑ Ⓒ Ⓓ

Constructed Response

14. _____
    _____

15. _____
    _____

Think Critically

16. _____
    _____

CHAPTER 21
Assessment | Student Recording Sheet

Section 21.3

Vocabulary Review

Write the vocabulary term that best matches each definition.

17. _____ 18. _____ 19. _____

Understand Key Concepts

Select the best answer from the choices given, and fill in the corresponding circle.

20. Ⓐ Ⓑ Ⓒ Ⓓ   21. Ⓐ Ⓑ Ⓒ Ⓓ   22. Ⓐ Ⓑ Ⓒ Ⓓ   23. Ⓐ Ⓑ Ⓒ Ⓓ

Constructed Response

24. _____

_____

25. _____

_____

Think Critically

26. _____

_____

Section 21.4

Vocabulary Review

Write the vocabulary term that makes each sentence true.

27. _____ 28. _____ 29. _____

Understand Key Concepts

Select the best answer from the choices given, and fill in the corresponding circle.

30. Ⓐ Ⓑ Ⓒ Ⓓ   31. Ⓐ Ⓑ Ⓒ Ⓓ   32. Ⓐ Ⓑ Ⓒ Ⓓ

Constructed Response

33. _____

_____

34. _____

_____

_____

CHAPTER 21
Assessment | Student Recording Sheet

Think Critically

35. _____
_____
_____

36. _____
_____

Additional Assessment

37. **Writing in Biology** Record your answer for question 37 on a separate sheet of paper.

Document-Based Questions

38. Record your answer for question 38 on a separate sheet of paper.

39. _____
_____
_____

40. _____
_____

Cumulative Review

41. _____
_____
_____

42. _____
_____

43. _____
_____

44. _____
_____
_____

CHAPTER 21
Assessment \ **Student Recording Sheet**

Standardized Test Practice

Multiple Choice

Select the best answer from the choices given, and fill in the corresponding circle.

1. Ⓐ Ⓑ Ⓒ Ⓓ   3. Ⓐ Ⓑ Ⓒ Ⓓ   5. Ⓐ Ⓑ Ⓒ Ⓓ   7. Ⓐ Ⓑ Ⓒ Ⓓ
2. Ⓐ Ⓑ Ⓒ Ⓓ   4. Ⓐ Ⓑ Ⓒ Ⓓ   6. Ⓐ Ⓑ Ⓒ Ⓓ   8. Ⓐ Ⓑ Ⓒ Ⓓ

Short Answer

Answer each question with complete sentences.

9. _____
_____

10. _____
_____
_____

11. Record your answer for question 11 on a separate sheet of paper.

12. Record your answer for question 12 on a separate sheet of paper.

13. _____
_____

14. _____
_____

15. _____

Extended Response

Answer each question with complete sentences.

16. _____
_____

17. _____
_____
_____

Essay Question

18. Record your answer for question 18 on a separate sheet of paper.

Table of Contents

Chapter 22 Plant Structure and Function

Diagnostic Test

CHAPTER 22
Plant Structure and Function

Before reading Chapter 22, predict answers to questions about the chapter content based on what you already know. Circle the letter of the correct answer, and then explain your reasoning.

1. Sonia's teacher asks the class to observe a potted plant and to identify several plant structures and their functions. What could be included in the list?
   - **A.** Roots absorb dissolved nutrients, stems provide support, and leaves make food.
   - **B.** Roots absorb water, hollow stems transport water, and leaves make food.
   - **C.** Roots make food, stem tissues transport food, and leaves collect water.
   - **D.** Roots transport water, stems provide support, and leaves collect food and water.

   Explain.

   _____

   _____

   _____

2. Tamara consults a tree identification guidebook to help her identify the trees growing in her neighborhood. Which information could be found in the guidebook?
   - **A.** All deciduous trees have the same arrangement of leaves on their stems.
   - **B.** Although tree leaves have the same color, their size, shape, and texture differ.
   - **C.** Most deciduous trees have leaves with parallel venation.
   - **D.** The blades of many tree leaves are divided into two or more leaflets.

   Explain.

   _____

   _____

   _____

3. How might the loss of a forest impact a region?

   _____

   _____

   _____

Launch Lab

What structures do plants have?

Most plants have structures that absorb light and others that take in water and nutrients. In this lab, you will examine a plant and observe and describe structures that help the plant survive.

Procedure 👓 👕 🧤

1. Read and complete the lab safety form.
2. Carefully examine a **potted plant** provided by your teacher. Use a **magnifying lens** to get a closer look. Make a list of each type of structure you observe.
3. Gently remove the plant from the pot and observe the plant structures in the soil. Do not break up the soil. Record your observations and place the plant back into the pot.
4. In the space below, sketch your plant and label each part.

Data and Observations

Analysis

1. **Compare** your list with those of other students. What structures were common to all plants?

   _____

   _____

2. **Infer** how each structure might be related to a function of the plant.

   _____

   _____

   _____

3. **Predict** the type of structural adaptations of plants living in dry environments.

   _____

   _____

   _____

MiniLab

CHAPTER 22
Observe Plant Cells

How can a microscope be used to distinguish plant cell types? Investigate the three different types of plant cells by making and observing slides of some common plant parts.

Procedure 🥽 👕 ⊘ 📋 ✋ ☠ ✋

WARNING: *Iodine is poisonous if swallowed and can stain skin and clothes.*

1. Read and complete the lab safety form.
2. Obtain a small, thin **slice of potato** and a thin **cross section of a celery stalk** from your teacher.
3. Place the potato slice on a **slide,** add a drop of **iodine,** and cover with a **coverslip.** Use a **microscope** to observe the potato slice. In the space below, record your observations.
4. Place the celery slice on a slide, add a drop of **water,** and cover with a coverslip.

5. Put a drop of **dye** at one end of the coverslip, and then touch a **paper towel** to the other end to draw the dye under the coverslip. Use a microscope to observe the celery slice. Record your observations.
6. Obtain a small amount of **pear tissue,** place it on a slide, and add a coverslip.
7. Using a **pencil eraser,** press gently but firmly on the coverslip until the pear tissue is a thin even layer. Use a microscope to observe the pear tissue. Record your observations.

Data and Observations

Analysis

1. **Identify** the type of specialized plant cell observed on each slide.

_____

_____

2. **Infer** why there are different cell types in a potato, a celery stalk, and pear tissue.

_____

_____

_____

MiniLab

CHAPTER 22

Investigate a Plant Response

What stimulus causes a Venus flytrap to shut its leaves? A Venus flytrap has specialized leaves that trap and digest insects. In this lab, you will learn what type of stimulus is necessary to trigger the trapping response.

Procedure 🔍 🧤 🖌

1. Read and complete the lab safety form.
2. Obtain a **Venus flytrap plant** with open leaves.
3. Using a **small paintbrush,** carefully touch one of the trigger hairs on the inner surface of a leaf. Record your observations below.

4. Wait 60 s. Now use your paintbrush and touch two different trigger hairs. Alternatively, touch one trigger hair and then touch it again in about ten seconds. Record your observations below.
5. After you have stimulated the leaves to snap shut, whenever possible, observe your plant to determine how long it takes the trap to open again. Write your data below.

Data and Observations

Analysis

1. **Identify** the type of stimulus necessary to trigger the plant leaf to shut. How long did it take the leaf to reopen?

_____

_____

2. **Think Critically** If you drop a dead insect onto a leaf, the leaf might close. However, it will not close tightly and will reopen later without digesting the insect. Based on this lab, hypothesize how the plant might distinguish between a living insect and a dead one.

_____

_____

_____

Design Your Own
BioLab

CHAPTER 22
Internet: How do dwarf plants respond to gibberellins?

Background: Some dwarf plants lack a gene for gibberellins production and some lack gibberellin receptors. In this lab, you will design an experiment to determine if you can change the growth pattern of dwarf pea-plant seedlings by applying gibberellic acid (a form of gibberellins) to them.

Question: *Can you use gibberellins to change the growth of dwarf pea plants?*

Materials
Choose materials that would be appropriate for this lab. Possible materials include:
gibberellic acid in varying concentrations
sheets of poster board or cardboard
dishwashing liquid (wetting agent)
potted dwarf pea-plant seedlings
spray bottles

cotton swabs
light source
large plastic bags
plant fertilizer
distilled water
metric rulers
graph paper

Safety Precautions 🥽 👕 🧤 ✋

Plan and Perform the Experiment
1. Read and complete the lab safety form.
2. Form a hypothesis that explains how gibberellins will affect the growth of dwarf pea plants.
3. Design an experiment to test your hypothesis. Be sure that your experiment has a control group.
4. Make a list of factors that must be constant for your experimental and control groups. Be sure to test only one variable.
5. Determine a way to apply gibberellins to the plants and decide how often you will apply it.
6. Design and construct a data table to record data from your experiment.

7. *Make sure your teacher approves your plan before you proceed.*
8. Collect the supplies you need and set up your experimental and control plants.
9. Complete the approved experiment.
10. Record measurements and observations of the plants in your data table.
11. Graph the data from your experimental and control groups.
12. **Cleanup and Disposal** Return unused gibberellic acid to your teacher for disposal. Empty spray bottles and thoroughly rinse. Dispose of used cotton swabs in the trash. Dispose of plants as directed by your teacher.

Data and Observations

Analyze and Conclude

1. **Analyze** your graph and determine the effect of gibberellic acid on the dwarf pea plants.

_____

_____

_____

2. **Hypothesize** Based on your results, explain why the pea plants are dwarfs.

_____

_____

_____

3. **Think Critically** Why might a genetic change, such as one that causes a plant not to produce gibberellins, be a problem for plants in a natural environment?

_____

_____

_____

4. **Error Analysis** What might have occurred in your experimental setup that could have caused your data to be inaccurate? How would you change your procedure?

_____

_____

_____

_____

_____

Real-World Biology: Analysis

CHAPTER 22
Controlling Weeds

People often complain about weeds in their gardens or lawns. They spend time pulling weeds and putting down a layer of mulch to try to keep weeds from growing. You have probably seen weeds growing along a road or in a vacant lot. Weeds seem to grow everywhere, but what type of plants are they? Weeds are any plants that grow where people don't want them.

Weeds in a garden or lawn can be unsightly and unwanted, but they do not cause serious problems. They can be removed by pulling them. However, weeds are a much larger problem in fields of crops, such as corn, potatoes, soybeans, and cotton. Weeds also can be a problem if they create a fire hazard in dry areas, block places to which people need access, or block people's vision on highways. In areas where weeds cannot be mowed, people often use weed killers, or herbicides, to control the weeds. Although different types of herbicides are used, the most common herbicides are synthetic auxins. Auxins are a type of plant hormone. In this activity, you will analyze the effects of a synthetic auxin on plants and decide how to get rid of weeds in different situations.

Synthetic Auxins

Synthetic auxins are manufactured chemicals that mimic indoleacetic acid (IAA). IAA is found in small quantities in plants. Applying large quantities of synthetic auxins to plants interrupts the plants' normal functioning, and the plants die. But people want only weeds to die, not their crops or lawns. Some auxin-based herbicides kill almost all the plants they come in contact with. Used incorrectly, most auxin-based herbicides can damage or kill plants that people don't want harmed. Used in the right amounts, auxin-based herbicides, such as 2,4-D, kill some types of plants but leave other types of plants unaffected.

Figure 1 shows the control group and the experimental group following an experiment in which corn plants and bean plants were sprayed with 2,4-D. Corn is a monocot, or a flowering plant whose embryos have only one seed leaf. Wheat and orchids are also monocots. Beans are eudicots, or flowering plants whose embryos have two seed leaves. Tomatoes and oaks are also eudicots. Study the illustration, and then respond to each statement and question.

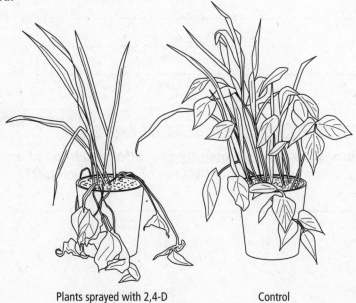

Plants sprayed with 2,4-D　　　　　Control

Figure 1

Analyze and Conclude

Respond to each question and statement.

1. **Describe** what happened to the corn and bean plants in **Figure 1** that were treated with 2,4-D.

_____

_____

2. **Explain** why a control was needed in the experiment.

_____

_____

3. **Generalize** Other experiments show that tomatoes and oaks treated with 2,4-D die, but wheat and orchids are not affected. Based on what you know about auxins, monocots, and eudicots, what type of plants does 2,4-D kill?

_____

_____

4. **Apply** Dandelions are eudicots, and grass is a monocot. You have been asked to get rid of dandelions growing in a lawn. What are two ways you could kill the dandelions without killing the grass? Explain.

_____

_____

_____

5. **Infer** If you had a small garden, what would be a disadvantage of planting corn and tomatoes close to each other?

_____

_____

_____

CAREERS IN BIOLOGY

Plant Biology Visit biologygmh.com for information on plant biologists. What are the responsibilities of a plant biologist?

_____

Enrichment

Analyze a Problem: Studying Plants for New Compounds

All organisms have evolved methods for protecting themselves from pests. Animals can run away or fight back. But, as your text explains, plants are sessile, anchored to the ground and unable to escape from a predator. Therefore, plants are limited to the production of chemical compounds that repel, disable, or kill the pests that attack them.

Scientists have learned that the chemicals produced by plants are often effective against humans pests. If those chemicals can be extracted from plants and purified, they can be used to treat human diseases or can be used against agricultural pests.

The study of medicines extracted from plants is a promising field of research. The development of a new drug in the laboratory usually takes many years and costs hundreds of millions of dollars. But the world is full of plants that have evolved mechanisms that use chemicals to fight off disease. Present-day science probably knows about only a fraction of the plant-based drugs that could be used for medical treatments. Searching for new plants with new chemical defense mechanisms might be far less expensive and more productive than focusing entirely on laboratory research for the development of new drugs.

The use of chemicals derived from plants could also revolutionize agriculture. It is usually safer and often less expensive to use natural products, such as chemicals derived from plants, to fight pests in the field than it is to use synthetic chemicals.

Research

The table lists some of the chemical compounds found in plants with medicinal or agricultural value for humans. Select any one of the compounds listed, or choose one of your own, to study in more detail. Consult reference books to find out how the compound was discovered and how it is being used by humans.

Summarize your research by writing a short proposal to the National Science Foundation in which you explain why the search for plant-based drugs and insecticides is a wise way of spending research funds in the United States.

Compound	Use
Agrimophol	anthelmintic
Benzyl benzoate	scabicide and pediculicide
Emetine	amoebicide
Glaucarubin	amoebicide
Hemsleyadin	treatment for dysentery
Kaibic acud	ascaricide
Nicotine	insecticide
Quinine	antimalarial agent
Rotenone	insecticide
Santonin	ascaricide
Taxol	anticancer agent
Thymol	antifungal agent
Your choice: _____	

Concept Mapping

Complete the network tree about the structure of plants. These terms may be used more than once: food, leaves, minerals, photosynthesis, provide support, roots, sclerenchyma cells, stems, water, xylem.

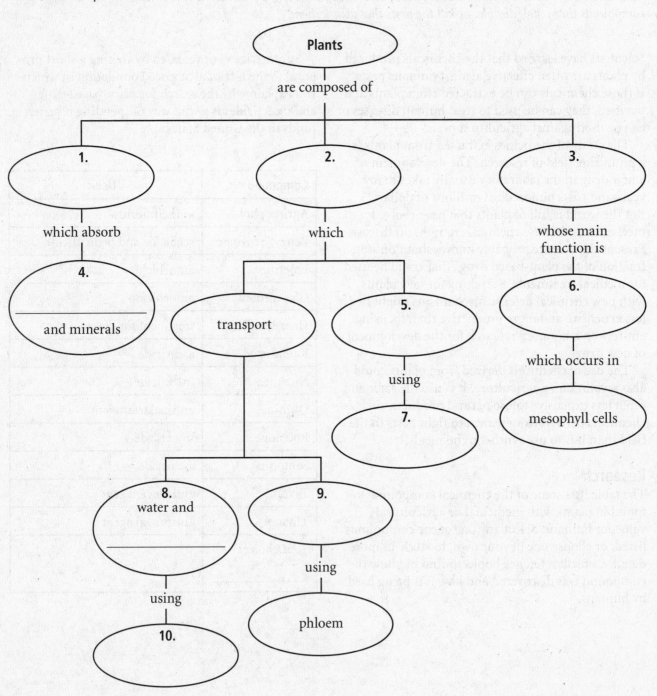

Study Guide

CHAPTER 22
Section 1: Plant Cells and Tissues

In your textbook, read about plant cells.

Label the diagram of the plant cell. Use these choices:

cell wall   central vacuole   chloroplast   nucleus   plasma membrane

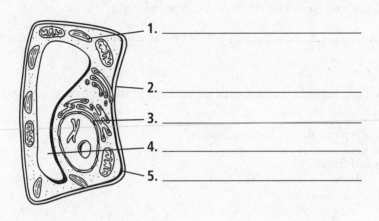

1. _____

2. _____

3. _____

4. _____

5. _____

Match the definition in Column A with the term in Column B.

Column A	Column B
_____ **6.** cells in the long strings that are part of celery stalks	**A.** collenchyma
_____ **7.** cells in which photosynthesis and food storage occur	**B.** sclerenchyma
_____ **8.** cells that provide strength such as sclereids and fibers	**C.** parenchyma

In the space at the left, write the letter of the term or phrase that best answers each question.

_____ **9.** In which type of plant cell are starch, water, and oils stored?
  A. collenchyma   **C.** parenchyma
  B. fibers   **D.** sclereids

_____ **10.** Which type of plant cells provides tough, protective coverings for seeds?
  A. collenchyma   **C.** parenchyma
  B. fibers   **D.** sclereids

_____ **11.** Which is a function of sclereids?
  A. food storage   **C.** photosynthesis
  B. gas exchange   **D.** transport

_____ **12.** Which characteristic does collenchyma give to a plant?
  A. color   **C.** height
  B. flexibility   **D.** taste

In your textbook, read about plant tissues.

Write the term or phrase that best completes each statement. Use these choices:

apical meristems	cork cambium	intercalary meristems	vascular cambium

13. A meristematic tissue that produces cells that develop tough cell walls is a(n)

_____ .

14. _____ cause roots and stems to increase in length.

15. Many monocots have _____ , which produce new cells at one or more

locations along a stem.

16. Some roots and stems have a(n) _____ that produces new xylem and phloem.

Label the diagram of the cross section of a plant stem. Use these choices:

dermal tissue   **ground tissue**

17. _____

18. _____

If the statement is true, write true. *If the statement is false, replace the italicized term or phrase to make it true.*

19. The cuticle helps *decrease* water loss by slowing evaporation.

_____

20. *Stomata* can give leaves a fuzzy appearance and can help protect the plant
from predators.

_____

21. Water and minerals are transported from the roots by *xylem* tissue.

_____

22. Sieve-tube members and companion cells make up *xylem* tissue.

_____

23. Most of a plant consists of *meristematic* tissue.

_____

Study Guide

CHAPTER 22
Section 2: Roots, Stems, and Leaves

In your textbook, read about roots.

Label the diagram of the cross section of a dicot root. Use these choices:

| cortex | endodermis | epidermis | phloem | root hair | xylem |

1. _____

2. _____

3. _____

4. _____

5. _____

6. _____

In your textbook, read about stems.

Match the description in Column A with the term in Column B.

Column A

_____ 7. produces cells that increase the length of a stem

_____ 8. produces cells that increase the diameter of a stem

_____ 9. a specialized underground stem

_____ 10. a specialized aboveground stem

Column B

A. tuber

B. apical meristem

C. vascular cambium

D. runner

In your textbook, read about leaves.

Label the diagrams of a leaf and its internal structure. Use these choices:

| blade | palisade mesophyll | petiole | spongy mesophyll | stoma | vascular bundle |

11. _____

12. _____

13. _____

14. _____

15. _____

16. _____

Study Guide

Section 3: Plant Hormones and Responses

In your textbook, read about plant hormones.

Complete the table by checking the correct column(s) for each description.

Description	Auxin	Gibberellin	Ethylene	Cytokinin
1. Inhibits the dropping of fruit				
2. Affects the ripening of fruit				
3. Affects seed growth				
4. Influenced by the presence of auxin				
5. Stimulates the elongation of cells				
6. Is the only known gaseous hormone				
7. Creates apical dominance				
8. Stimulates cell division				

In your textbook, read about plant responses.

Write the term or phrase that best completes each statement. Use these choices:

gravitropism	nastic response	negative tropism	phototropism
positive tropism	solar tracking	thigmotropism	tropism

9. A _____ is a plant movement that is independent of the direction of the stimulus and is not a growth response.

10. Plant growth toward a stimulus is called _____ .

11. A vine can twist around a fence as it grows because of a _____ .

12. A _____ is a growth response to light caused by an unequal distribution of auxin.

13. Plants exhibit a _____ when they grow away from a stimulus.

14. A _____ is a plant's growth response to an external stimulus.

15. _____ is the motion of a sunflower in relation to the changing position of the Sun.

16. When roots grow down into the soil, they are exhibiting a positive _____ .

Copyright © Glencoe/McGraw-Hill, a division of The McGraw-Hill Companies, Inc.

Guía de estudio

CAPÍTULO 22

Sección 1: Células y tejidos de las plantas

En tu libro de texto, lee acerca de las células de las plantas.

Identifica el diagrama de la célula de la planta. Usa estas opciones:

cloroplasto	membrana plasmática	núcleo	pared celular	vacuola central

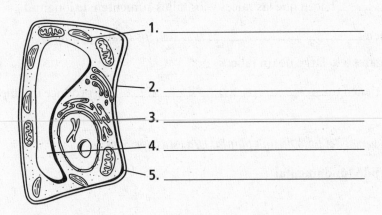

1. _____

2. _____

3. _____

4. _____

5. _____

Relaciona la definición de la columna A con el término de la columna B.

Columna A

Columna B

_____ 6. células en los hilos largos que son parte de los tallos de apio

_____ 7. células en las cuales ocurre la fotosíntesis y el almacenamiento de alimentos

_____ 8. células que dan fuerza como las esclereidas y fibras

A. colénquimas

B. esclerénquimas

C. parénquimas

En el espacio a la izquierda, escribe la letra del término o frase que mejor responda a cada pregunta.

_____ 9. ¿En qué tipo de célula de la planta se almacenan el almidón, el agua y los aceites?
A. colénquimas **C.** fibras
B. esclereidas **D.** parénquimas

_____ 10. ¿Qué tipo de célula de la planta proporciona una cubierta fuerte y protectora para las semillas?
A. colénquimas **C.** fibras
B. esclereidas **D.** parénquimas

_____ 11. ¿Cuál es una función de las esclereidas?
A. almacenamiento de comida **C.** intercambio de gases
B. fotosíntesis **D.** transporte

_____ 12. ¿Qué característica dan las colénquimas a una planta?
A. altura **C.** flexibilidad
B. color **D.** sabor

En tu libro de texto, lee acerca de los tejidos de las plantas.

Escribe el término o frase que mejor complete cada afirmación. Usa estas opciones:

cambium del corcho	**meristemas apicales**	**meristemas intercalares**	**cambium vascular**

13. Un tejido meristemático que produce células que desarrollan paredes celulares

fuertes es un _____ .

14. Los _____ hacen que las raíces y los tallos aumenten de longitud.

15. Muchas monocotiledóneas tienen _____ , los cuales producen

células nuevas en uno o más lugares a lo largo de un tallo.

16. Algunas raíces y algunos tallos tienen un _____ que produce un nuevo

xilema y floema.

Identifica el diagrama del corte transversal del tallo de una planta. Usa estas opciones:

tejido dérmico   **tejido fundamental**

17. _____

18. _____

Si la afirmación es verdadera, escribe «verdadero». Si la afirmación es falsa, sustituye el término o la frase en cursiva para volverla verdadera.

19. La cutícula ayuda a *disminuir* la pérdida de agua mediante la desaceleración de la evaporación.

_____

20. *La estomata* puede dar a las hojas un aspecto velloso y puede ayudar a proteger las plantas contra depredadores.

_____

21. El agua y los minerales se transportan desde las raíces a través del tejido *xilema*.

_____

22. Los miembros del tubo criboso y las células acompañantes componen el tejido *xilema*.

_____

23. La mayor parte de una planta consta de tejido *meristemático*.

_____

Guía de estudio

En tu libro de texto, lee acerca de las raíces.

Identifica el diagrama del corte transversal de una raíz dicótoma. Usa estas opciones:

córtex	endodermis	epidermis	floema	raicilla	xilema

1. _____

2. _____

3. _____

4. _____

5. _____

6. _____

En tu libro de texto, lee acerca de los tallos.

Relaciona la descripción de la columna A con el término de la columna B.

Columna A		Columna B
_____ 7. produce células que aumentan la longitud de un tallo		**A.** tubérculo
_____ 8. produce células que aumentan el diámetro de un tallo		**B.** meristema apical
_____ 9. es un tallo subterráneo especializado		**C.** cambium vascular
_____ 10. es un tallo superficial especializado		**D.** planta trepadora

En tu libro de texto, lee acerca de las hojas.

Identifica los diagramas de una hoja y su estructura interna. Usa estas opciones:

bulto vascular	estoma	lámina	mesófilo en empalizada	mesófilo esponjoso	petiolo

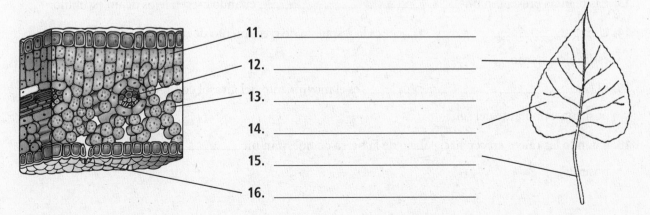

11. _____

12. _____

13. _____

14. _____

15. _____

16. _____

Guía de estudio

En tu libro de texto, lee acerca de las hormonas de las plantas.

Completa la tabla marcando la(s) columna(s) correcta(s) para cada descripción.

Descripción	Auxina	Giberelina	Etileno	Citoquinina
1. Inhibe la caída del fruto				
2. Afecta la maduración del fruto				
3. Afecta el crecimiento de la semilla				
4. Se ve influenciada por la presencia de auxina				
5. Estimula el estiramiento de las células				
6. Es la única hormona gaseosa conocida				
7. Crea dominación apical				
8. Estimula la división de las células				

En tu libro de texto, lee acerca de las respuestas de las plantas.

Escribe el término o la frase que mejor complete cada afirmación. Usa estas opciones:

fototropismo	gravitropismo	repuesta nástica	seguimiento solar
tigmotropismo	tropismo	tropismo negativo	tropismo positivo

9. Una _____ es el movimiento de una planta que es independiente de

   la dirección del estímulo y no es una respuesta de crecimiento.

10. El crecimiento de la planta en dirección a un estímulo es un _____ .

11. Una planta trepadora se enrolla alrededor de una cerca a medida que crece debido a un

    _____ .

12. Un _____ es una repuesta de crecimiento a la luz causada por una

    distribución desigual de auxina.

13. Las plantas presentan un _____ cuando crecen lejos de un estímulo.

14. Un _____ es la respuesta de crecimiento de una planta a un

    estímulo externo.

15. El (La) _____ es el movimiento del girasol con relación a la

    posición cambiante del sol.

16. Cuando las raíces crecen hacia abajo de la tierra demuestran un _____

    positivo.

Section
Quick Check

CHAPTER 22
Section 1: Plant Cells and Tissues

After reading the section in your textbook, respond to each statement.

1. **Name** the type of plant tissue where photosynthesis takes place.

   _____

2. **State** the main way in which sclerenchyma cells differ from collenchyma cells and parenchyma cells.

   _____

   _____

3. **Discuss** the nature and function of three types of specialized structures of the plant epidermis.

   _____

   _____

   _____

   _____

   _____

   _____

4. **Compare** and **contrast** the vessel elements and sieve-tube members in plant vascular tissue.

   _____

   _____

   _____

   _____

5. **Predict** how damage to the vascular tissues of a plant could affect the plant.

   _____

   _____

   _____

Section Quick Check

Section 2: Roots, Stems, and Leaves

After reading the section in your textbook, respond to each statement.

1. **List** two functions of roots.

_____

2. **Describe** the layered structure of a root.

_____

_____

_____

3. **Summarize** the two different ways in which stems can grow.

_____

_____

_____

_____

4. **Determine** leaf adaptations for photosynthesis. Use the terms *blade, palisade mesophyll, spongy mesophyll,* and *stomata* in your answer.

_____

_____

_____

_____

_____

5. **Recommend** the type of root system that a crop planted to control erosion should have. Explain the reasons for your choice.

_____

_____

_____

Section
Quick Check

Section 3: Plant Hormones and Responses

After reading the section in your textbook, respond to each statement.

1. Specify three characteristics of nastic responses.

_____

_____

2. Explain how ethylene's gaseous state affects its transport.

_____

_____

3. Choose a plant hormone to use in experiments to make a newly discovered dwarf plant grow taller.

_____

_____

_____

_____

4. Differentiate between cytokinins and auxins in terms of how they promote plant growth.

_____

_____

5. Determine whether phototropism is a positive or negative tropic response. Explain.

_____

_____

Chapter Test **A**

CHAPTER 22
Plant Structure and Function

Part A: Multiple Choice

In the space at the left, write the letter of the term or phrase that best completes each statement or answers each question.

_____ **1.** Collenchyma, parenchyma, and sclerenchyma are examples of plant _____
   A. cells.
   B. fibers.
   C. hormones.
   D. tissues.

_____ **2.** What is a small opening in leaves that allows gases to pass in and out of a plant?
   A. cell plate
   B. petiole
   C. stomata
   D. trichome

_____ **3.** If carrot plants had fibrous roots instead of taproots, they would **not** be able to _____
   A. absorb necessary amounts of water.
   B. create their own oxygen and sugar.
   C. store large amounts of food.
   D. transport water and minerals.

Part B: Matching

Matching Set 1 *Write the letter of the correct plant tissue on the line next to the description of its function. Answers may be used only once.*

_____ **1.** have diverse functions such as photosynthesis   **A.** ground tissues

_____ **2.** transport food and water throughout the plant   **B.** meristematic tissues

_____ **3.** produce new cells to increase plant length   **C.** vascular tissues

Matching Set 2 *Write the letter of the correct plant hormone or group of hormones on the line next to the description of its function. Answers may be used only once.*

_____ **4.** causes plant cells to lengthen   **A.** auxins

_____ **5.** ripens the fruit of plants   **B.** cytokins

_____ **6.** promotes plant cell division   **C.** ethylene

Chapter Test **A** CONTINUED

Part C: Interpreting Drawings

*Use **Figure 1** to respond to the following statement.*

1. **Identify** the cortex, endodermis, epidermis, phloem, and xylem on the drawing of a dicot root.

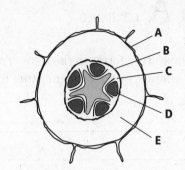

A. _____

B. _____

C. _____

D. _____

E. _____

Figure 1

*Use **Figure 2** to respond to the following statement.*

2. **Compare** and **contrast** the characteristics of the leaves of shagbark hickory, sugar maple, and horse chestnut trees shown in the drawings. Use the terms *compound leaves, opposite arrangement, simple leaves, venation,* and *whorled arrangement* in your discussion.

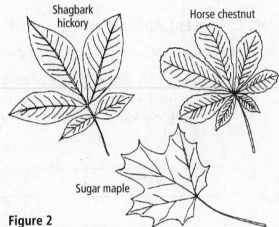

Shagbark hickory

Horse chestnut

Sugar maple

Figure 2

_____

_____

_____

_____

Part D: Short Answer

Write your response to each statement in the space provided.

1. **Discuss** the basic function of plant stems. Include the term *vascular tissue* in your discussion.

_____

_____

_____

2. **Compare** and **contrast** tuber, bulb, and rhizome stems.

_____

_____

_____

3. An annual growth ring forms in the stem of a woody plant such as an oak tree. **Infer** how the amount of available moisture might affect the width of an oak tree's annual rings.

_____

_____

_____

Part E: Concept Application

Write your response to each statement in the space provided.

1. Tropical rain forests receive 250 cm or more of rain every year. **Evaluate** the effect of rain forest deforestation (cutting down trees in the rain forest) on the annual rainfall of tropical rain forest regions. Include the term *transpiration* in your discussion.

_____

_____

_____

_____

2. Astronauts aboard the space shuttle often take plants such as tomato plants aboard to conduct experiments in the near-zero gravity environment of space. **Predict** the growth response of the tomato plants in these conditions.

_____

_____

_____

_____

Chapter Test **B**

Copyright © Glencoe/McGraw-Hill, a division of The McGraw-Hill Companies, Inc.

CHAPTER 22
Plant Structure and Function

Part A: Multiple Choice

In the space at the left, write the letter of the phrase that best completes each statement or answers each question.

_____ 1. Which is **not** a characteristic of a typical plant cell?
   A. contains chloroplasts
   B. eventually loses cytoplasm
   C. has a large central vacuole
   D. surrounded by a cell wall

_____ 2. Sclerenchyma plant cells _____
   A. are spherical in shape with thin cell walls.
   B. have an elongated shape and can be stretched.
   C. lack living components when they mature.
   D. maintain the greatest variety of organelles.

_____ 3. What is the function of parenchyma cells?
   A. accelerate plant growth in stems and roots
   B. form wood to support the entire plant
   C. provide support for surrounding cells
   D. undergo cell division to help repair a plant

_____ 4. If a sunflower plant lost all of its collenchyma cells, it would _____
   A. fall over.
   B. lose petals.
   C. stop growing.
   D. turn brown.

_____ 5. Which help mangrove trees increase their oxygen supply?
   A. adventitious roots
   B. fibrous roots
   C. pneumatophore roots
   D. taproots

Part B: Matching and Completion

Matching *Write the letter of the correct type of stem on the line next to the description of its function. Answers may be used only once or not at all.*

_____ 1. horizontal stem growing on soil surface   A. bulb

_____ 2. swollen underground stem of a potato plant   B. corm

_____ 3. shortened, compressed stem surrounded by leaves C. rhizome

_____ 4. horizontal stem growing underground   D. stolon

                                                              E. tuber

Chapter Test B CONTINUED

Completion *Write the correct plant hormone(s) to complete each sentence below.*

5. The plant hormone(s) found in rapidly growing tissues is (are) called

_____ .

6. Fruits would not ripen without the gaseous plant hormone(s) called

_____ .

7. Plants cells would have difficulties completing the processes of mitosis and cytokinesis without the

hormone(s)_____ .

8. Dwarf bonsai trees would most likely lack the hormone(s) _____ .

Part C: Interpreting Drawings

*Use **Figure 1** to respond to the following statement.*

1. **Identify** the five major root structures on the drawing of a dicot root.

   A. _____

   B. _____

   C. _____

   D. _____

   E. _____

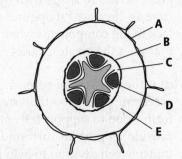

Figure 1

*Use **Figure 2** to respond to the following statement.*

2. **Compare** and **contrast** the characteristics of the leaves of a shagbark hickory, sugar maple, and horse chestnut trees shown in the drawings. In your response, identify simple and compound leaves and discuss the arrangement and venation of each leaf type.

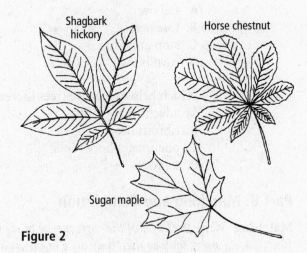

Shagbark hickory

Horse chestnut

Sugar maple

Figure 2

_____

_____

_____

_____

_____

Chapter Test B CONTINUED

Part D: Short Answer

Write your response to each statement in the space provided.

1. **Compare** and **contrast** apical meristem tissue, intercalary meristem tissue, and lateral meristem tissue.

_____

_____

_____

2. **Describe** the path that water takes as it enters and exits a maple tree.

_____

_____

_____

3. **Discuss** the leaf modifications of poison ivy and squash plants that are designed to prevent organisms from touching or eating their leaves.

_____

_____

_____

Part E: Concept Application

Write your response to each statement in the space provided.

1. A farmer discovers a fungus that is destroying some of the root hairs of his primary crop. **Infer** how the fungus might affect the growth of his crop.

_____

_____

_____

2. **Evaluate** Tropical rain forests receive 250 cm or more of rain every year. Evaluate the effect of rain forest deforestation on the average annual rainfall of rain forest regions and on the quality of water in the regions' streams and rivers. Include the term *transpiration* in your discussion.

_____

_____

_____

Chapter Test C

Plant Structure and Function

Part A: Multiple Choice

In the space at the left, write the letter of the term or phrase that best completes each statement or answers each question.

_____ 1. Which are found only in plant cells?
   A. different-colored pigments
   B. large, central vacuole
   C. membrane-bound nucleus
   D. thick, viscous cytoplasm

_____ 2. If a sunflower plant lost all of its collenchyma cells, it would be unable to _____
   A. absorb vital nutrients and minerals.
   B. collect large quantities of water.
   C. grow new cells on its stem and root tips.
   D. support the weight of its flower.

_____ 3. Without cork cambium, a sugar maple tree would _____
   A. absorb smaller quantities of water and dissolved substances.
   B. be infested with fungi and insects eating away at its wood.
   C. fall over as its roots rotted and decayed beneath the soil.
   D. lose its leaves during the summer months instead of autumn.

_____ 4. Which is the function of the root cap?
   A. absorb water and nutrients
   B. promote root growth
   C. protect root tissues
   D. transport dissolved substances

_____ 5. The stem of a white potato plant is a _____
   A. bulb.
   B. corm.
   C. stolon.
   D. tuber.

_____ 6. Which type of stem is most vulnerable to being damaged by a person walking on it?
   A. bulb
   B. rhizome
   C. stolon
   D. tuber

Part B: Completion

Write the correct term or phrase to complete each sentence below.

1. Plant cells that serve as the basis for many plant structures and are capable of a wide variety of

   functions are called _____ .

Chapter Test **C** CONTINUED

2. Plant cells that are vital for the construction industry of the United States are called

_____ .

3. Plant tissues that enable grass plants to increase in length after they have been mowed are called

_____ .

4. Water vapor, oxygen, and carbon dioxide pass out of a plant's leaves through the

_____ .

5. Plants with soft, flexible stems that are capable of photosynthesis are called

_____ .

6. The blade of a willow tree is attached to the stem by a stalk called

a(n) _____ .

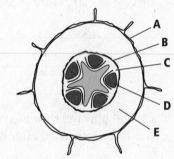

Part C: Interpreting Drawings

*Use **Figure 1** to respond to each statement.*

1. **Identify** the five major root structures on the drawing of a dicot root.

Figure 1

A. _____   D. _____

B. _____   E. _____

C. _____

2. **Infer** how the function of the root would be impacted in the absence of each of these structures.

_____

_____

_____

*Use **Figure 2** to respond to the following statement.*

3. **Compare** and **contrast** the characteristics of the leaves in the drawings.

_____

_____

_____

_____

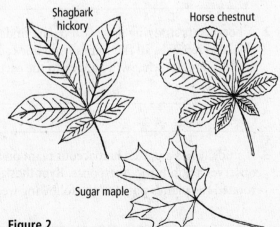

Shagbark hickory

Horse chestnut

Sugar maple

Figure 2

Chapter Test C CONTINUED

Part D: Short Answer

Write your response to each statement in the space provided.

1. **Describe** the functions of the meristem tissue in a white oak tree.

   _____

   _____

   _____

2. **Discuss** the structure of xylem and its components.

   _____

   _____

   _____

   _____

3. **Explain** how the flow of xylem and phloem through a tree enables the age of a tree to be estimated after it has been cut down.

   _____

   _____

   _____

   _____

Part E: Concept Application

Write your response to each statement in the space provided.

1. **Evaluate** the effects of rain forest deforestation based on the loss of specific plant structures and functions of rain forest plants from the ecosystem.

   _____

   _____

   _____

2. A botanist is studying desert cacti. She finds two identical cacti growing side by side. She removes all the spines from one cactus plant. The other plant serves as a control. **Predict** what will happen to the cactus plant without spines.

   _____

   _____

3. A student sets a potted herbaceous plant on a windowsill for a week and observes a phototropic response. **Hypothesize** what the student would observe if he rotated the plant's pot 180° the following week.

   _____

   _____

CHAPTER 22
Assessment Student Recording Sheet

Section 22.1
Vocabulary Review

Explain the difference between the vocabulary terms in each pair.

1. _____
_____

2. _____
_____

3. _____
_____

Understand Key Concepts

Select the best answer from the choices given, and fill in the corresponding circle.

4. Ⓐ Ⓑ Ⓒ Ⓓ   6. Ⓐ Ⓑ Ⓒ Ⓓ   8. Ⓐ Ⓑ Ⓒ Ⓓ

5. Ⓐ Ⓑ Ⓒ Ⓓ   7. Ⓐ Ⓑ Ⓒ Ⓓ

Constructed Response

9. _____
_____

10. _____
_____
_____
_____

11. _____
_____
_____

Think Critically

12. Record your answer for question 12 on a separate sheet of paper.

13. _____
_____
_____
_____

CHAPTER 22
Assessment   Student Recording Sheet

Section 22.2

Vocabulary Review

Write a sentence for each set of terms.

14. _____

_____

15. _____

_____

16. _____

_____

Understand Key Concepts

Select the best answer from the choices given, and fill in the corresponding circle.

17. Ⓐ Ⓑ Ⓒ Ⓓ   19. Ⓐ Ⓑ Ⓒ Ⓓ   21. Ⓐ Ⓑ Ⓒ Ⓓ

18. Ⓐ Ⓑ Ⓒ Ⓓ   20. Ⓐ Ⓑ Ⓒ Ⓓ

Constructed Response

22. _____

_____

_____

23. _____

_____

Think Critically

24. Record your answer for question 24 on a separate sheet of paper.

25. _____

_____

Section 22.3

Vocabulary Review

Write sentences to compare and contrast each pair of terms.

26. _____

_____

27. _____

_____

CHAPTER 22
Assessment | Student Recording Sheet

28. _____

_____

Understand Key Concepts

Select the best answer from the choices given, and fill in the corresponding circle.

29. Ⓐ Ⓑ Ⓒ Ⓓ   **31.** Ⓐ Ⓑ Ⓒ Ⓓ   **33.** Ⓐ Ⓑ Ⓒ Ⓓ

30. Ⓐ Ⓑ Ⓒ Ⓓ   **32.** Ⓐ Ⓑ Ⓒ Ⓓ

Constructed Response

34. Record your answer for question 34 on a separate sheet of paper.

35. _____

_____

36. _____

_____

_____

Think Critically

37. Record your answer for question 37 on a separate sheet of paper.

38. _____

_____

39. Careers in Biology _____

_____

_____

Additional Assessment

40. Writing in Biology Record your answer for question 40 on a separate sheet of paper.

Document-Based Questions

41. _____

_____

42. _____

_____

Cumulative Review

43–44. Record your answers for questions 43 and 44 on a separate sheet of paper.

CHAPTER 22
Assessment \ Student Recording Sheet

Standardized Test Practice

Multiple Choice

Select the best answer from the choices given, and fill in the corresponding circle.

1. Ⓐ Ⓑ Ⓒ Ⓓ
2. Ⓐ Ⓑ Ⓒ Ⓓ

3. Ⓐ Ⓑ Ⓒ Ⓓ
4. Ⓐ Ⓑ Ⓒ Ⓓ

5. Ⓐ Ⓑ Ⓒ Ⓓ
6. Ⓐ Ⓑ Ⓒ Ⓓ

7. Ⓐ Ⓑ Ⓒ Ⓓ
8. Ⓐ Ⓑ Ⓒ Ⓓ

Short Answer

Answer each question with complete sentences.

9. _____

10. _____
_____
_____

11. _____
_____

12. Record your answer for question 12 on a separate sheet of paper.

13. _____
_____
_____

14. _____
_____
_____

Extended Response

Answer each question with complete sentences.

15. _____
_____

16. _____
_____

17. _____
_____

Essay Question

18. Record your answer for question 18 on a separate sheet of paper.

Table of Contents

Chapter 23 Reproduction in Plants

Diagnostic Test

CHAPTER 23

Reproduction in Plants

Before reading Chapter 23, predict answers to questions about the chapter content based on what you already know. Circle the letter of the correct answer, and then explain your reasoning.

1. While visiting his grandparents' farm, Den's grandfather explains how various crops are grown. He also explains basic facts about plant reproduction and life cycles. Which does he tell Den?

   A. All plants grow from seeds that form after fertilization.

   B. Many plants, such as potatoes, can grow from plant parts.

   C. Plants must reproduce offspring using sexual reproduction.

   D. Seed-bearing fruits are reproductive structures of all plants.

   Explain.

   _____

   _____

   _____

2. Manuel takes a guided hike at the nature center near his home, and he learns about the life cycle of white pine trees. Which does he learn?

   A. Cones are produced by small, conifer flowers.

   B. Conifer trees produce male and female cones.

   C. Pine seeds are produced in cones without gametes.

   D. Pine trees do not produce sperm cells inside pollen.

   Explain.

   _____

   _____

   _____

3. While working for a florist, Melanie learns about the basic structures of a flower. About what structures does she learn?

   _____

   _____

   _____

Launch **Lab**

CHAPTER 23
What are plant reproductive structures?

Have you ever noticed that sometimes flowers seem to appear suddenly on trees, shrubs, and other plants in the spring? Have you picked up a cone while walking under pine trees and wondered why these trees have cones? Like many organisms, plants have reproductive structures and reproduce sexually. Mosses, ferns, gymnosperms, and angiosperms have unique reproductive structures. Investigate these structures during this lab.

Procedure

1. Read and complete the lab safety form.
2. Create a data table to record your observations and measurements of the plant reproductive structures your teacher gives you.

3. Observe the reproductive structures of a **moss, fern, conifer,** and **flowering plant.** Record your observations in your data table.

Data and Observations

Analysis

1. **Identify** the similarities and differences in the reproductive structures of the plants.

_____

_____

_____

2. **Describe** how flowering plants might use flowers to reproduce based on what you already know about plants.

_____

_____

_____

MiniLab

Compare Conifer Cones

How do cones from the different conifers compare? Have you ever noticed the many different types of cones that fall from conifers? Investigate the types of cones during this lab.

Procedure 👓 🧤 🧹

1. Read and complete the lab safety form.
2. Create a data table for recording your observations, measurements, and comparisons of cones.
3. Obtain **cones** from your teacher.
4. Observe the physical characteristics of your cones and record your observations and measurements in your data table. Do not damage the cones in any way.

5. Identify the conifer species of your cones by using a **tree identification guidebook.** Record this data.
6. Return the cones to your teacher.

Data and Observations

Analysis

1. **Compare** and **contrast** the cones.

_____

_____

2. **Describe** Were there any seeds present? How do you think seeds form in conifers?

_____

_____

_____

MiniLab

CHAPTER 23

Compare Flower Structures

How do the structures of flowers vary? Just a quick browse through a flower garden or florist's shop reveals that there is great diversity among flowers. Investigate how flowers differ from species to species.

Procedure 🥽 🧤 🔬

1. Read and complete the lab safety form.
2. Create a data table to record your observations and measurements.
3. Obtain the **flowers** for this lab from your teacher.

4. Observe the differences in structure, color, size, and odor of the flowers. Do not damage the flowers in any way.
5. Make a sketch of each flower and record other observations in your data table.
6. Return the flowers to your teacher.

Data and Observations

Analysis

1. **Compare** and **contrast** the flower structures you observed.

_____

_____

_____

2. **Infer** why the flower petals that you observed were different colors.

_____

_____

3. **Propose** an explanation for the different sizes and shapes of flower structures.

_____

_____

_____

Design Your Own
BioLab

CHAPTER 23
How do monocot and eudicot flowers compare?

Background: Flowers are the reproductive structures of flowering plants, and there is great diversity in flower form. Botanists classify flowering plants into two groups—monocots and eudicots—based on the structure of their seeds. However, their flower structures also differ. Explore the differences between these two groups of plants by completing this lab.

Question: *What are the structural differences between monocot and eudicot flowers?*

Materials
Choose materials that would be appropriate for this lab. Possible materials include:
monocot flowers
eudicot flowers
colored pencils

Safety Precautions 🥽 👔 ✋
WARNING: *Use dissecting tools with extreme caution.*

Plan and Perform the Experiment
1. Read and complete the lab safety form.
2. Choose several features of monocot and eudicot flowers to observe and compare.
3. Create a data table to record your observations of flowers—monocots and eudicots. Include sketches of each flower type.
4. Make sure your teacher approves your plan before you proceed.
5. Make observations as you planned.

6. **Label** and color-code the female and male reproductive structures and other flower parts of one of your monocot flower sketches.
7. Repeat step 6 using one of the eudicot flower sketches.
8. **Cleanup and Disposal** Properly dispose of the flower parts. Clean all equipment as instructed by your teacher and return everything to its proper storage location.

Data and Observations

Analyze and Conclude

1. **Compare** and **contrast** the characteristics of monocot and eudicot flowers.

_____

_____

_____

_____

_____

2. **Conclude** Which of the flowers that you examined were monocots? Eudicots?

_____

_____

3. **Error Analysis** Compare your data with the data collected by your classmates. Explain any differences.

_____

_____

_____

Real-World Biology: Lab

CHAPTER 23
Variables Affecting Seed Germination

Many people grow flowering plants from seeds. They might plant seeds to grow flowers, such as zinnias and cosmos, or they might plant seeds to grow vegetables, such as cucumbers and radishes. Planting seeds is easy. Yet, many people have trouble getting seeds to germinate. They might plant the seeds too early in the spring, when the soil is too cold. They might plant them too deep or too shallow. They might give them too much or not enough water.

Another problem could be with the seeds themselves, instead of how they were planted. For example, the seeds could be too old, or they could have been kept in poor conditions. In this activity, you will choose a variable that might affect seed germination and perform an experiment to test the variable.

Procedure

1. Read and complete the lab safety form.
2. Choose a variable that might affect seed germination. Some possible variables are temperature, depth of planting, type of soil, amount of water, and soaking or not soaking seeds before planting. Write a hypothesis about how the variable you chose affects seed germination.
3. You will use **two cups** and plant **five seeds in each cup.** Write a list of other materials you will need.
4. On a separate sheet of paper, write the procedure you will follow to test your hypothesis. Make sure to include a control and explain how the control and experimental seeds will be treated.

5. Obtain the two cups, ten seeds, and any other materials you need. Write your name on both cups.
6. Follow your procedure for planting five seeds in one of the cups. Write *control* on the cup.
7. Follow your procedure for planting five seeds in the second cup. Write *variable* on the cup.
8. Follow the rest of your procedure.
9. Observe your cups every day for three weeks. Record in **Table 1** the number of seeds germinated each day. Also record any other observations you make about the germinating seeds.

Table 1: Number of Seeds Germinated							
	Day 1	Day 2	Day 3	Day 4	Day 5	Day 6	Day 7
Control							
Variable							
	Day 8	Day 9	Day 10	Day 11	Day 12	Day 13	Day 14
Control							
Variable							
	Day 15	Day 16	Day 17	Day 18	Day 19	Day 20	Day 21
Control							
Variable							

Analyze and Conclude

Respond to each question.

1. **Summarize** How did the number of experimental (variable) seeds that germinated compare to the number of control seeds that germinated?

   _____

   _____

2. **Conclude** Based on your data, how does the variable you tested affect the germination of seeds? Was your hypothesis correct?

   _____

   _____

   _____

   _____

3. **Analyze** Why do you think you got the results you did?

   _____

   _____

   _____

   _____

4. **Evaluate** How would you change your experiment to try to get more information on the effects of the variable you tested?

   _____

   _____

   _____

   _____

5. **Infer** Look at the results of your classmates' experiments. What general conclusions can you draw about seed germination?

   _____

   _____

   _____

   _____

CAREERS IN BIOLOGY

Agronomy Visit biologygmh.com for information on seed scientists. What are the responsibilities of a seed scientist?

Enrichment

Group Project: Plants for Every Use

Humans in every culture have learned to use plants for almost every conceivable use. The field of biology devoted to the study of human use of plants is called ethnobotany (ethno, "the study of people," and botany, "the study of plants"). Ethnobotanists visit cultures in every part of the world to discover how people use plants for foods, seasonings, medicines, ornamentations, religious practices, and other applications.

Select Working in a small group, select one of the flowering plants listed in the table to research. For example, one group might research big bluestem, while another group researches sweet alyssum. You can also choose another plant to research.

Research Once you have selected a flowering plant, use your textbook and other reference materials to find information. Your research should include information about the plant's flowers and possible uses of the plant. Look for photographs of the plants. Fill in the table for the plant your group has chosen.

Present Finally, present the information that you learned about the plant. Show any photographs of the plant that you found. As other groups give their presentations, complete the table. After all groups have given their presentations, have a class discussion about questions class members might have.

Common Name	Scientific Name	Flower Description	Possible Uses of Plant
Rattlesnake master			
Jack-in-the-pulpit			
Big bluestem			
Sweet alyssum			
Maca			
Epazote			
Your own choice: _____			

Concept Mapping

Plant Reproduction

Complete the cycle map about plant reproduction. These terms may be used more than once: cell division, diploid zygote, eggs, fertilization, gametophytes, haploid gametes, haploid spores.

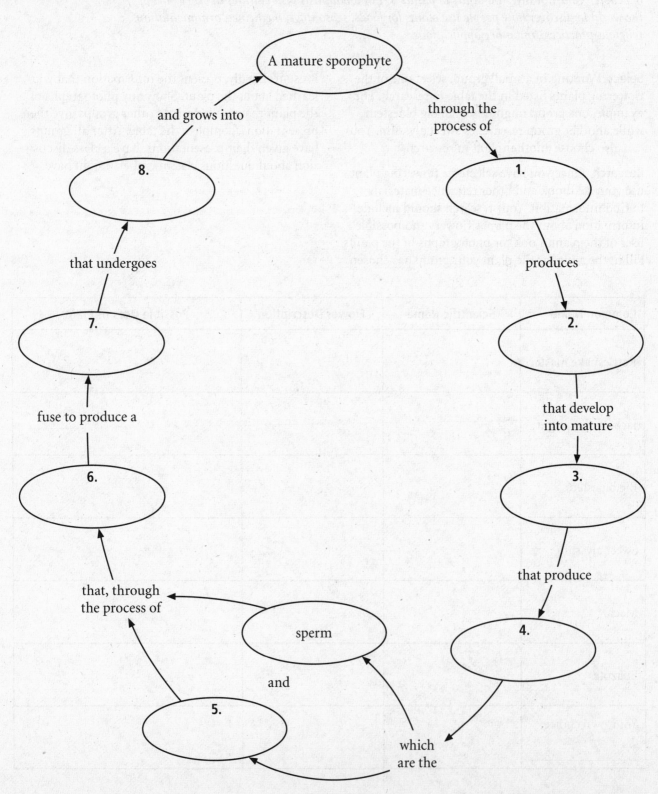

A mature sporophyte

and grows into

through the process of

8.

1.

that undergoes

produces

7.

2.

fuse to produce a

that develop into mature

6.

3.

that, through the process of

that produce

5.

4.

sperm

and

which are the

Study Guide

Section 1: Introduction to Plant Reproduction

In your textbook, read about vegetative reproduction.

If the statement is true, write true. *If the statement is false, replace the italicized word or phrase to make it true.*

1. Vegetative reproduction is a form of *sexual* reproduction in which new plants grow from parts of an existing plant.

   _____

2. New plants produced vegetatively are *clones* of the original plant.

   _____

3. Not all plants form seeds in their *fruits*, so these plants reproduce by vegetative reproduction.

   _____

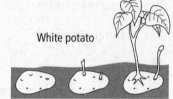

White potato

4. The figure shows a potato plant being reproduced *vegetatively*.

   _____

5. The process of growing a plant from a few cells of plant tissue is called *rooting stem cuttings*.

   _____

In your textbook, read about alternation of generations and moss reproduction and life cycle.

Write the term that best completes each statement. Use these choices:

chemotaxis	**diploid**	**egg**	**gametophyte**	**largest**
meiosis	**nonvascular**	**sperm**	**sporophyte**	

6. The two phases of the plant life cycle are the _____ stage and the

   _____ stage.

7. The cells of the sporophyte are all _____ .

8. The female gamete is the _____ , and the male gamete is the

   _____ .

9. The sperm of _____ plants must have at least a film of water to reach an egg.

10. Mosses belong to one of the few plant divisions in which the gametophyte is the

    _____ phase.

11. Spores are produced by _____ in the capsule of the moss sporophyte.

12. Sperm produced in antheridia move toward eggs produced in archegonia in a process

    called _____ .

In your textbook, read about fern reproduction and life cycle.

Match the definition in Column A with the term in Column B.

Column A   **Column B**

_____ **13.** spore-producing structures   **A.** rhizome

_____ **14.** a tiny, heart-shaped gametophyte structure   **B.** zygote

_____ **15.** structures that produce flagellated sperm   **C.** sori

_____ **16.** the first cell of the sporophyte generation   **D.** antheridia

_____ **17.** an underground stem that supports fronds   **E** prothallus

In your textbook, read about conifer reproduction and life cycle.

Write the term that best completes each statement. Use these choices:

heterosporous	**megaspores**	**micropyle**	**microspores**

18. A _____ plant produces two types of spores that

develop into male or female gametophytes.

19. Cells in the sporangia of the pollen-producing cone undergo meiosis and form

_____ .

20. The opening of the ovule of a conifer is called a _____ .

21. A cell in the ovule undergoes meiosis and forms four _____ .

Label the diagram of structures in the conifer life cycle. Use these choices:

female cone   **male cone**   **mature sporophyte**

22. _____

23. _____

24. _____

Study Guide

In your textbook, read about flower organs and flower adaptations.

Label the diagram of a flower. Use these choices:

anther   filament   ovary   ovule   petal   sepal   stigma

1. _____

2. _____

3. _____

4. _____

5. _____

6. _____

7. _____

Respond to each statement.

8. **Name** the type of flower that has both pistils and stamens. _____

9. **Identify** the type of plants whose flowers have parts in multiples of three. _____

In your textbook, read about pollination mechanisms.

For each answer below, write an appropriate question.

10. **Answer:** They are brightly colored, have strong scents, and make a sweet liquid called nectar.

    Question: _____

11. **Answer:** A plant's flowers pollinate themselves or other flowers on the same plant.

    Question: _____

In your textbook, read about photoperiodism.

Use each of the terms below only once to complete the passage.

day-neutral   intermediate-day   long-day   short-day

Different kinds of plants can bloom at different times of the year because of photoperiodism.

A **(12)** _____ plant blooms when exposed to more than the critical

number of hours of darkness. A **(13)** _____ plant blooms when exposed

to fewer than the critical number of hours of darkness. Plants that bloom regardless of the length

of days and nights are called **(14)** _____ plants. Many tropical plants are

(15) _____ plants.

Study Guide

CHAPTER 23
Section 3: Flowering Plants

In your textbook, read about flowering plants.

Match the definition in Column A with the term in Column B.

	Column A		Column B
_____	**1.** two nuclei in the center of the cell		**A.** dormancy
_____	**2.** process in which one sperm fertilizes the egg and the other sperm joins with the central cell		**B.** double fertilization
_____	**3.** food-storing tissue that supports the development of the embryo		**C.** endosperm
_____	**4.** period of inactivity that can occur in seeds		**D.** germination
_____	**5.** occurs when an embryo in a seed starts to grow into a new plant		**E.** polar nuclei

In your textbook, read about the results of reproduction.

Write the phrase that best completes each statement. Use these choices:

aggregate fruits   **dry fruits**   **multiple fruits**   **simple fleshy fruits**

6. _____ are dry when they are mature. Examples include pods, nuts, and grains.

7. _____ form from flowers with multiple female organs that fuse as the fruits ripen. Examples include strawberries, raspberries, and blackberries.

8. _____ form from many flowers that fuse as the fruits ripen. Examples are figs, pineapples, mulberries, and Osage oranges.

9. _____ can contain one or more seeds. Examples are apples, peaches, and grapes.

Label the diagram showing eudicot seed germination. Use these choices:

cotyledon   **embryo**   **first leaves**   **hypocotyl**   **radicle**   **seed coat**

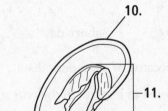

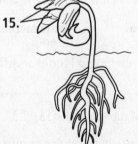

10. _____	12. _____	14. _____
11. _____	13. _____	15. _____

Guía de estudio

CAPÍTULO 23

Sección 1: Introducción a la reproducción de las plantas

En tu libro de texto, lee acerca de la reproducción vegetativa.

Si la afirmación es verdadera, escribe «verdadero». Si la afirmación es falsa, substituye la palabra o frase en cursiva para volverla verdadera.

1. La reproducción vegetativa es una forma de reproducción *sexual* en la cual las plantas nuevas crecen de las partes de una planta existente.

_____

2. Las plantas nuevas producidas de forma vegetativa son *clones* de la planta original.

_____

3. Las plantas que no forman semillas en sus *frutos* se reproducen mediante reproducción vegetativa.

_____

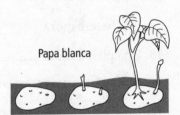

Papa blanca

4. El dibujo muestra una planta de papa que se reproduce de *forma vegetativa*.

_____

5. Cultivar una planta a partir de células se llama *cortes de tallo enraizado*.

_____

En tu libro de texto, lee acerca de la alternación de generaciones y de la reproducción y el ciclo de vida de los musgos.

Escribe el término o frase que mejor complete cada afirmación. Usa estas opciones:

diploides	esperma	esporofito	gametofito	huevo
más larga	meiosis	no vasculares	quimiotaxis	

6. Las dos fases del ciclo de vida de la planta son la etapa del _____ y la etapa

del _____ .

7. Las células del esporofito son todas _____ .

8. El gameto femenino es el _____ , y el gameto masculino es

el _____ .

9. El esperma de las plantas _____ debe tener agua para alcanzar al huevo.

10. El musgo pertenece a una de las pocas divisiones de plantas de las cuales el gametofito es la

fase _____ .

11. Las esporas del musgo se producen mediante _____ .

12. El esperma se mueve hacia los huevos mediante un proceso llamado _____

En tu libro de texto, lee acerca de la reproducción de los helechos y del ciclo de vida.

Relaciona la definición en la columna A con el término en la columna B.

Columna A	Columna B

Columna A

_____ **13.** estructuras que producen esporas

_____ **14.** una estructura pequeña de gametofitos en forma de corazón

_____ **15.** estructuras que producen esperma flagelado

_____ **16.** la primera célula de la generación de esporofitos

_____ **17.** un tallo subterráneo que soporta las frondas

Columna B

A. rizoma

B. zigoto

C. soros

D. anteridios

E. protalo

En tu libro de texto, lee acerca de la reproducción de las coníferas y del ciclo de vida.

Escribe el término que mejor complete cada afirmación. Usa estas opciones:

heterospora **megasporas** **micrófilo** **microsporas**

18. Una planta _____ produce dos tipos de esporas que se desarrollan en gametofitos masculinos o femeninos.

19. Las células en los esporangios del cono productor de polen pasan por el proceso de meiosis y forman _____ .

20. La abertura del óvulo de una conífera se llama _____ .

21. Una célula en el óvulo pasa por el proceso de meiosis y forma cuatro _____ .

Identifica el diagrama de las estructuras en el ciclo de vida de las coníferas. Usa estas opciones:

cono femenino **cono masculino** **esporofito maduro**

22. _____

23. _____

24. _____

Guía de estudio

En tu libro de texto, lee acerca de los órganos de la flor y las adaptaciones de la flor.

Identifica el diagrama de una flor. Usa estas opciones:

antera	filamento	estigma	ovario	óvulo	pétalo	sépalo

1. _____

2. _____

3. _____

4. _____

5. _____

6. _____

7. _____

Responde a cada afirmación.

8. **Nombra** el tipo de flor que tiene tanto pistilos como estambre. _____

9. **Identifica** el tipo de plantas cuyas flores tienen partes en múltiplos de tres. _____

En tu libro de texto, lee acerca de los mecanismos de polinización.

Para cada respuesta a continuación, escribe una pregunta apropiada.

10. **Respuesta:** Son de colores brillantes, tienen olores fuertes y producen un líquido dulce llamado néctar.

    Pregunta: _____

11. *Respuesta:* Las flores de una planta se polinizan a sí mismas o a otras flores en la misma planta.

    Pregunta: _____

En tu libro de texto, lee acerca de la fotoperiodicidad.

Usa los siguientes términos sólo una vez para completar el párrafo.

día corto	día intermedio	día largo	día neutro

Los diferentes tipos de plantas pueden florecer en diferentes épocas del año debido a la fotoperiodicidad.

Una planta de (**12**) _____ florece cuando se expone a más horas del número

crítico de horas de oscuridad. Una planta de (**13**) _____ florece cuando se

expone a menos horas del número crítico de horas de oscuridad. Las plantas que florecen sin importar la

duración de los días y las noches se llaman plantas de (**14**) _____ . Muchas

plantas tropicales son plantas de (**15**) _____ .

Guía de estudio

En tu libro de texto, lee acerca de las plantas con flores.

Relaciona la definición de la columna A con el término de la columna B.

Columna A

_____ **1.** dos núcleos en el centro de la célula

_____ **2.** proceso en el cual un esperma fertiliza al huevo y el otro esperma se une con la célula central

_____ **3.** tejido que almacena alimento para el embrión

_____ **4.** periodo de inactividad que puede ocurrir en las semillas

_____ **5.** ocurre cuando un embrión en una semilla empieza a crecer para convertirse en una nueva planta

Columna B

A. latencia

B. fertilización doble

C. endosperma

D. germinación

E. núcleos polares

En tu libro de texto, lee acerca de los resultados de la reproducción.

Escribe la frase que mejor complete cada afirmación. Usa estas opciones:

frutos agregados   **frutos carnosos simples**   **frutos múltiples**   **frutos secos**

6. Los _____ son secos cuando se maduran. Un ejemplo es los granos.

7. Los _____ se forman de flores con órganos femeninos múltiples que se fusionan a medida que los frutos se maduran. Un ejemplo es la fresa.

8. Los _____ se forman cuando flores se fusionan. Un ejemplo es el higo.

9. Los _____ pueden contener una o más semillas. Unos ejemplos son las manzanas, los duraznos y las uvas.

Identifica el diagrama que muestra la germinación de semilla eudicotiledóneas. Usa estas opciones:

cotiledón   cubierta de la semilla   embrión   hipocotilo   primeras hojas   radícula

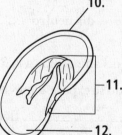

10. _____

11. _____

12. _____

13. _____

14. _____

15. _____

Section Quick Check

Section 1: Introduction to Plant Reproduction

After reading the section in your textbook, respond to each statement.

1. **Recall** why the life cycle of plants is referred to as having an alternation of generations.

   _____

   _____

   _____

2. **Explain** why a film of water is needed for fertilization in nonvascular plants.

   _____

   _____

   _____

   _____

   _____

3. **Contrast** the sporophyte generations of mosses and ferns.

   _____

   _____

   _____

   _____

4. **Determine** which generation of a conifer is dependent on the other.

   _____

   _____

5. **Hypothesize** which type of reproduction (vegetative or sexual) is preferable when a plant with a new, desirable characteristic has been developed. Explain.

   _____

   _____

   _____

   _____

Section Quick Check

After reading the section in your textbook, respond to each statement.

1. Describe the structure of a stamen.

_____

_____

_____

_____

2. Identify the nonreproductive organs of a flower.

_____

_____

3. Utilize what you know about plant adaptations to identify how flowers that lack petals and that produce huge amounts of pollen are pollinated. Explain.

_____

_____

_____

_____

_____

4. Infer the effect that exposing a short-day plant to long days will have on the plant.

_____

_____

5. Predict the kind of pollination that is most likely to occur in plants with imperfect flowers. Justify your prediction.

_____

_____

_____

Section
Quick Check

CHAPTER 23
Section 3: Flowering Plants

After reading the section in your textbook, respond to each statement.

1. List the main events that occur in the germination of a seed.

_____

_____

_____

2. Discuss the differences between a monocot seed and a eudicot seed.

_____

_____

3. Differentiate between pollination and fertilization.

_____

_____

_____

_____

4. Compare and **contrast** seeds and fruits.

_____

_____

_____

_____

5. Assess possible advantages of dormancy in seeds.

_____

_____

_____

Chapter Test **A**

CHAPTER 23

Reproduction in Plants

Part A: Multiple Choice

In the space at the left, write the letter of the term or phrase that best answers each question.

_____ **1.** Which is an example of vegetative reproduction?
   A. crossing two different types of vegetables
   B. growing a potato from a cubed potato
   C. joining the egg and sperm of a tomato plant
   D. reproducing simple moss plants from spores

_____ **2.** Which describes the process of plant fertilization?
   A. a flower turning into the fruit of a plant
   B. a seed growing into a plant when buried
   C. pollen grains landing on a plant's flower
   D. the joining of a plant's egg and sperm

_____ **3.** Which is a simple fleshy fruit?
   A. apple
   B. blackberry
   C. cashew
   D. pineapple

Part B: Matching

Write the letter of the correct type of plant on the line next to its description. Answers may be used only once.

_____ **1.** a plant that flowers when exposed to 16 h of darkness   **A.** day-neutral plant

_____ **2.** a plant that only flowers in the summer   **B.** long-day plant

_____ **3.** a plant that flowers in any amount of darkness   **C.** short-day plant

Part C: Interpreting Drawings

Use the illustration to the right to respond to the following statement.

1. Identify the flower parts labeled *A*, *B*, and *C*.

   A. _____

   B. _____

   C. _____

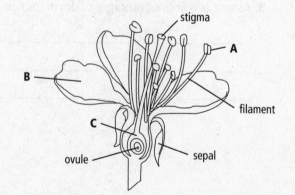

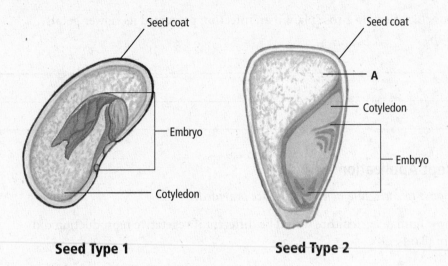

Seed Type 1   **Seed Type 2**

Use the illustrations above to respond to each statement.

2. **Identify** the two types of seeds labeled *Seed Type 1* and *Seed Type 2* in the drawings above.

Seed Type 1: _____   Seed Type 2: _____

3. **Identify** the structure labeled *A* that distinguishes the two types of seeds, and explain the function of the structure.

_____

_____

_____

Part D: Short Answer

Write your response to each statement in the space provided.

1. **Differentiate** between male and female conifer cones.

_____

_____

_____

2. **Describe** the process of pollination. Include the term *stigma* in your answer.

_____

_____

_____

Chapter Test A CONTINUED

3. **Infer** the possible effect on a rose plant if an infection prevented its flower petals from forming.

_____

_____

_____

Part E: Concept Application

Write your response to each statement in the space provided.

1. **Appraise** how human agriculture would be different if vegetative reproduction did not occur in plants.

_____

_____

_____

2. A farmer plants corn seeds into the ground when the soil is at an optimum temperature for germination. **Interpret** how soaking the soil with water causes the plants to grow. Use the term *germination* in your answer.

_____

_____

_____

Chapter Test **B**

CHAPTER 23
Reproduction in Plants

Part A: Multiple Choice

In the space at the left, write the letter of the term or phrase that best completes each statement or answers each question.

_____ **1.** Which describes the life cycle of a plant that has an alternation of generations?
   A. a diploid sporophyte stage and diploid gametophyte stage
   B. a diploid sporophyte stage and haploid gametophyte stage
   C. a haploid sporophyte stage and diploid gametophyte stage
   D. a haploid sporophyte stage and haploid gametophyte stage

_____ **2.** Flowers without petals are called _____
   A. complete flowers.
   B. eudicot flowers.
   C. incomplete flowers.
   D. monocot flowers.

_____ **3.** Which structure protects the bud of the flower?
   A. petal
   B. pistil
   C. sepal
   D. stamen

_____ **4.** A plant that requires 17.5 h of darkness each day is called a(n) _____
   A. day-neutral plant.
   B. intermediate-day plant.
   C. long-day plant.
   D. short-day plant.

_____ **5.** Which is the primary purpose of seed dispersal?
   A. begin photosynthesis in the seed coat
   B. create a new colony of offspring plants
   C. lure animals away from the parent plant
   D. reduce competition with the parent plant

Part B: Matching and Completion

Matching *Write the letter of the correct plant life cycle on the line next to its description. Answers may be used only once or not at all.*

_____ **1.** Spores develop into a thin, threadlike structure called a protonema.

_____ **2.** A structure called a prothallus is part of its life cycle.

_____ **3.** Two types of spores are produced that develop into male and female gametes.

A. anthophyte life cycle

B. conifer life cycle

C. fern life cycle

D. moss life cycle

Chapter Test **B** CONTINUED

Completion *Write the correct term in the blank to complete each sentence below.*

4. Plants, such as conifers, that produce two different types of spores that develop into male and female gametophytes are referred to as _____ .

5. The female reproductive structure of a flower is called the _____ .

6. The response of a morning-glory flower to the number of hours of uninterrupted darkness in a day is called _____ .

7. The nuclei in the center of a megaspore are called _____ .

Part C: Interpreting Drawings

Use the illustration to the right to respond to the following statement.

1. Identify the flower parts labeled *A–E.*

   A. _____

   B. _____

   C. _____

   D. _____

   E. _____

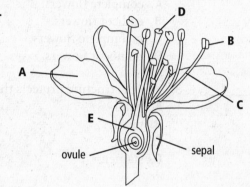

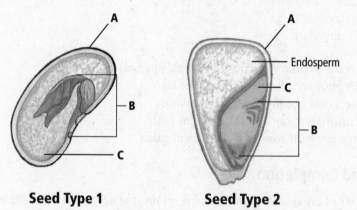

Seed Type 1   **Seed Type 2**

Use the illustrations above to respond to each statement.

2. **Identify** the two types of seeds labeled *Seed Type 1* and *Seed Type 2* in the drawings above.

   Seed Type 1: _____   Seed Type 2: _____

3. **Identify** the structures *A–C* that both seeds have in common.

   A. _____   B. _____   C. _____

Chapter Test B CONTINUED

Part D: Short Answer

Write your response to each statement in the space provided.

1. **Contrast** the mechanisms plants use for pollination.

   _____

   _____

   _____

2. **Infer** the effect of low oxygen levels on the germination process of a bean seed. Use the term *cellular respiration* in your answer.

   _____

   _____

   _____

Part E: Concept Application

Write your response to each statement in the space provided.

1. Strawberry plants extend horizontal stems called runners along the surface of the ground to reproduce new plants through the process of vegetative reproduction. **Infer** several advantages of this reproductive method over reproduction using seeds.

   _____

   _____

   _____

2. Fossilized, microscopic pollen grains are common in layers of sedimentary rock. **Develop** a strategy paleontologists could use to infer the climate of ancient periods of Earth's history using fossilized pollen grains.

   _____

   _____

   _____

Chapter Test **C**

CHAPTER 23
Reproduction in Plants

Part A: Multiple Choice

In the space at the left, write the letter of the term, phrase, or sentence that best completes each statement or answers each question.

_____ 1. Which statement is true of the overall life cycle of moss plants?
   A. After fertilization, the first sporophyte stage results in a protonema.
   B. In most moss species, the rhizoid produces millions of eggs.
   C. The gametophyte stage of the plant is most commonly observed.
   D. The mature sporophyte produces antheridia and archegonia.

_____ 2. Heterosporous plants, such as pine trees, produce two different types of _____
   A. cones.
   B. eggs.
   C. seeds.
   D. spores.

_____ 3. A flower that has only sepals and stamens is called a(n) _____
   A. complete flower.
   B. imperfect flower.
   C. incomplete flower.
   D. perfect flower.

_____ 4. Which type of flower would be produced by a tropical plant that is pollinated by fruit bats?
   A. fragrant red flowers
   B. fragrant white flowers
   C. odorless red flowers
   D. odorless white flowers

_____ 5. Which describes tomato plants that can flower in both 8 h of daylight and 14 h of daylight?
   A. day-neutral plants
   B. intermediate-day plants
   C. long-day plants
   D. short-day plants

_____ 6. Which type of fruit is a pineapple?
   A. aggregate fruit
   B. dry fruit
   C. fleshy fruit
   D. multiple fruit

Part B: Completion

Write the correct term in the blank to complete each sentence below.

1. In damp soil, a fern spore grows into a gametophyte structure called

   a(n) _____ .

2. The female reproductive structure of a flower is called the _____ .

Chapter Test **C** CONTINUED

3. A plant with flowers that have nine petals is called a(n) _____ .

4. Flower adaptations offer different pollination mechanisms for species of plants classified

as _____ .

5. A flower's response to the number of hours of darkness each day is called

_____ .

6. The first structure out of a seed that eventually will form the plant's roots is called

the _____ .

Part C: Interpreting Drawings

Use the illustration to the right to respond to the following statement.

1. Identify the flower parts labeled *A–G*.

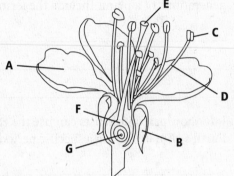

A. _____   E. _____

B. _____   F. _____

C. _____   G. _____

D. _____

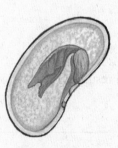

Seed Type 1   **Seed Type 2**

Use the illustrations above to respond to each statement.

2. Identify the two types of seeds labeled *Seed Type 1* and *Seed Type 2* in the drawings above.

Seed Type 1: _____   Seed Type 2: _____

3. Compare and **contrast** the structures of the two seeds.

_____

_____

_____

Chapter Test C CONTINUED

Part D: Short Answer

Write your response to each statement in the space provided.

1. **Compare** and **contrast** vegetative reproduction and crossbreeding.

_____

_____

_____

2. **Distinguish** between the gametophyte and sporophyte stages of an alternation of generations of a plant. Include the terms *haploid* and *diploid* in your answer.

_____

_____

_____

3. **Infer** how paleontologists can use the exine of fossilized pollen grains to determine Earth's climate during a specific period of prehistory.

_____

_____

_____

Part E: Concept Application

Write your response to each statement in the space provided.

1. While watching pollen-laden bees fly from flower to flower, a science student assumes that the bees are causing fertilization that soon will result in the creation of seeds. **Assess** the science student's assumption.

_____

_____

2. **Conclude** how seeds dispersed by wind would differ from seeds dispersed by animals.

_____

_____

_____

3. In 1982, seeds of the East Indian lotus plant were grown after they had been discovered in a 466-year-old archeological site. **Consider** how these lotus plants could grow after such a long period of time.

_____

_____

CHAPTER 23
Assessment | Student Recording Sheet

Section 23.1

Vocabulary Review

Write the vocabulary term that makes each sentence true.

1. _____ 2. _____ 3. _____

Understand Key Concepts

Select the best answer from the choices given, and fill in the corresponding circle.

4. Ⓐ Ⓑ Ⓒ Ⓓ   5. Ⓐ Ⓑ Ⓒ Ⓓ   6. Ⓐ Ⓑ Ⓒ Ⓓ   7. Ⓐ Ⓑ Ⓒ Ⓓ

Constructed Response

8. _____
_____
_____

9. _____
_____
_____
_____

10. _____
_____

Think Critically

11. _____
_____
_____

12. _____
_____

Section 23.2

Vocabulary Review

Explain the difference between the vocabulary terms in each pair.

13. _____
_____

CHAPTER 23
Assessment | Student Recording Sheet

14. _____

_____

15. _____

_____

Understand Key Concepts

Select the best answer from the choices given, and fill in the corresponding circle.

16. Ⓐ Ⓑ Ⓒ Ⓓ   18. Ⓐ Ⓑ Ⓒ Ⓓ   20. Ⓐ Ⓑ Ⓒ Ⓓ

17. Ⓐ Ⓑ Ⓒ Ⓓ   19. Ⓐ Ⓑ Ⓒ Ⓓ

Constructed Response

21. _____

_____

22. _____

_____

_____

23. _____

_____

Think Critically

24. Record your answer for question 24 on a separate sheet of paper.

25. _____

_____

_____

Section 23.3
Vocabulary Review

Explain the relationship between the vocabulary terms in each pair.

26. _____

_____

27. _____

_____

28. _____

CHAPTER 23
Assessment Student Recording Sheet

Understand Key Concepts

Select the best answer from the choices given, and fill in the corresponding circle.

29. Ⓐ Ⓑ Ⓒ Ⓓ   31. Ⓐ Ⓑ Ⓒ Ⓓ   33. Ⓐ Ⓑ Ⓒ Ⓓ

30. Ⓐ Ⓑ Ⓒ Ⓓ   32. Ⓐ Ⓑ Ⓒ Ⓓ

Constructed Response

34. _____
_____
_____

35. _____
_____

36. _____
_____

Think Critically

37. Record your answer for question 37 on a separate sheet of paper.

38. Record your answer for question 38 on a separate sheet of paper.

39. _____
_____

Additional Assessment

40. **Writing in Biology** Record your answer for question 40 on a separate sheet of paper.

Document-Based Questions

41. _____
_____

42. _____
_____

43. Record your answer for question 43 on a separate sheet of paper.

Cumulative Review

44. _____
_____

45. Record your answer for question 45 on a separate sheet of paper.

46. _____

CHAPTER 23
Assessment   Student Recording Sheet

Standardized Test Practice

Multiple Choice

Select the best answer from the choices given, and fill in the corresponding circle.

1. Ⓐ Ⓑ Ⓒ Ⓓ   3. Ⓐ Ⓑ Ⓒ Ⓓ   5. Ⓐ Ⓑ Ⓒ Ⓓ   7. Ⓐ Ⓑ Ⓒ Ⓓ

2. Ⓐ Ⓑ Ⓒ Ⓓ   4. Ⓐ Ⓑ Ⓒ Ⓓ   6. Ⓐ Ⓑ Ⓒ Ⓓ   8. Ⓐ Ⓑ Ⓒ Ⓓ

Short Answer

Answer each question with complete sentences.

9. _____

_____

10. _____

_____

11. _____

_____

12. _____

_____

13. Record your answer for question 13 on a separate sheet of paper.

14. _____

_____

15. _____

Extended Response

Answer each question with complete sentences.

16. _____

_____

17. _____

_____

18. Record your answer for question 18 on a separate sheet of paper.

19. Record your answer for question 19 on a separate sheet of paper.

Essay Question

20. Record your answer for question 20 on a separate sheet of paper.

Diagnostic Test

Page 3

1. The correct answer is C. Based on student responses, use the list below to address preconceptions.

   - **Student thinks leaves take in water vapor.** Direct student to the plant adaptations to land environments discussion in Section 21.1.

   - **Student thinks leaves take in water.** Direct student to the plant adaptations to land environments discussion in Section 21.1.

   - **Student thinks plants do not have tissues or organs.** Explain to student that, like animals, plants have specialized tissues and organs, such as vascular tissues and roots, to perform specific functions.

   - **Student thinks water is not required for the process of photosynthesis.** Explain to student that sunlight, carbon dioxide, and water are the required ingredients for photosynthesis.

   - **Student thinks plant leaves have no openings.** Introduce student to the term stomata and direct student to the plant adaptations to land environments discussion in Section 21.1.

   - **Student thinks all plants use osmosis or diffusion to transport water through their bodies.** Direct student to the plant adaptations to land environments discussion in Section 21.1.

2. The correct answer is D. Based on student responses, use the list below to address preconceptions.

   - **Student thinks flowering plants are classified into several divisions.** Direct student to the plant classification discussion in Section 21.1.

   - **Student thinks deciduous trees are not flowering plants.** Explain to student that most deciduous trees produce flowers and are classified as flowering plants. The flowers of many deciduous trees are small and not easily noticed.

   - **Student thinks Kingdom Plantae is divided into phyla instead of divisions.** Direct student to the plant classification discussion in Section 21.1.

   - **Student thinks mosses or ferns are not plants.** Direct student to the plant classification discussion in Section 21.1.

   - **Student thinks all seedless plants are classified into one group.** Direct student to the plant classification discussion in Section 21.1.

   - **Student thinks cone-bearing plants are classified into one division.** Direct student to the plant classification discussion in Section 21.1.

3. Annual plants complete their life span in one growing season or less. Many garden plants and weeds are annuals. Biennials have a two-year life span. The first year is devoted to growing roots and leaves. Carrots, beets, and turnips are biennials. Perennials live several years, but usually grow flowers and produce seeds every year. Sometimes they survive unfavorable conditions by dropping their leaves or allowing the above-ground structures to die. Based on student responses, use the list below to address preconceptions.

   - **Student thinks annual plants always live for one year.** Direct student to the Division Anthophyta discussion in Section 21.3.

   - **Student confuses the life cycles of annuals, biennials, and perennials.** Direct student to the Division Anthophyta discussion in Section 21.3.

   - **Student confuses the types of plants classified as annuals, biennials, and perennials.** Direct student to the Division Anthophyta discussion in Section 21.3.

   - **Student thinks all plants have an extended life cycle of several years or more.** Direct student to the Division Anthophyta discussion in Section 21.3.

Launch Lab

Page 4 • What characteristics differ among plants?

Analysis

1. Answers will vary depending upon students' lists.

2. Answers will vary based on plants chosen for the study, but students should recognize that there is diversity within the plant kingdom.

3. Students should recognize that the presence and absence of leaves, flowers, pollen, fruit, and seeds may vary seasonally. Students might also

suggest that classifying plants according to molecular/genetic characteristics might be helpful.

MiniLab

Page 5 • Compare Plant Cuticles

Analysis

1. lettuce leaves; yes, the data should support this observation.

2. Students should infer that the leaves that lost the least amount of water had more cuticle.

MiniLab

Page 6 • Investigate Conifer Leaves

Analysis

1. Grouping system should be based on conifer leaf characteristics.

2. Accept any reasonable explanation.

BioLab

Page 7 • Field Investigation: How can you identify and classify trees?

Analyze and Conclude

1. Answers will vary based on the study area chosen. Students should recognize that tree diversity can be relatively high, even within a small area.

2. Characteristics used in tree identification should be included in the dichotomous key. Characteristics will most likely be related to leaf type and placement, bark, flowers, fruit, and tree size.

3. Answers will vary based on the dichotomous key developed.

4. Answers will vary but might include choosing a different defining characteristic for step 1 of the key, and narrowing or widening the scope of one or more characteristics identified at specific steps.

Real-World Biology: Analysis

Page 9 • Plants for Gardens and Landscapes

Planning the Activity

Have students complete this activity after they have studied the classification of plants in Chapter 21 of the text.

Purpose

Students will investigate ways to group plants other than by using scientific names.

Career Applications

An interest in plants could lead to a career as a horticulturist. Horticulture is the science and art of growing fruits, vegetables, and flowers, or ornamental plants. A horticulturist might develop new plants, conduct experiments to improve plants, or develop better ways to grow plants. Many career choices are available within this field, such as retail garden center management, nursery management, sports field or golf course management, greenhouse management, organic farming, sales, landscape design, landscape construction and maintenance, plant science research, and teaching. A horticulturist can also work for universities, private research groups, government agencies, consulting agencies, nurseries, seed companies, and tree farms. A college degree is usually required, but many related jobs require a high school diploma or a two-year degree.

Teaching Strategies

- Ask students "What plants do you like?" "What are the characteristics of your favorite plant?"

- Discuss where students see plants growing and how the areas differ.

- Ask students to share experiences looking at plants in a greenhouse, nursery, garden store, or catalog.

- If possible, bring seed and flower catalogs to class that use scientific names and the names of cultivars and varieties.

- Below Level: Students might think that all members of a species are exactly the same. Remind them that there is variation within all species. These variations can be fairly significant, yet the different varieties are all the same species.

- Above Level: Have students research the different varieties of *Brassica olerocea*. If possible, supply students with samples from the grocery store and have them compare and contrast the varieties.

Answers to Student Worksheet

Part A: Other Ways to Group Plants
Analyze and Conclude

1. Answers could include what type of plants the person wants, how long the plant's life span is, how much sunlight the plant needs, how much moisture the plant needs, and how big the plant grows.

2. If you were choosing plants to grow under large trees, you would need to consider how much sunlight the area gets and how much sunlight the plants need.

Part B: Cultivars and Varieties
Analyze and Conclude

1. Plant 2 is a cultivar because it has a name in single quotes after its scientific name.

2. For Plant 3, *Brassica* is the genus name, *oleracea* is the species name, and *botrytis* is the variety name.

3. A cultivar is a group of plants that has been developed from a species and maintained by cultivation of specific characteristics. It does not exist in nature. A variety is a subspecies of a natural species. It is different enough to have a separate name, but not different enough to be a separate species.

Careers in Biology

A horticulturist can develop new plants, conduct experiments to improve plants, or develop better ways to grow plants.

Enrichment

Page 11 • Plant Classification and Use

Student presentations might vary but should be accurate and complete. Presentations should include detailed information on the classifications, habitats, and uses of the plants. Photographs of the plants would be useful illustrations for the presentations. Prickly pear cactus, purple coneflower, white willow, and Mormon tea all are commonly used for medicinal purposes. Ponderosa pines and redwoods are used for lumber. Peat moss is used in gardens. The fruits of the prickly pear cactus are edible.

Common Name	Nonvascular/ Vascular	Division	Scientific Name
Common liverwort	nonvascular	Hepaticophyta	*Marchantia polymorpha*
California redwood	vascular	Coniferophyta	*Sequoia sempervirens*
Mormon tea	vascular	Gnetophyta	*Ephedra sp.*
Peat moss	nonvascular	Bryophyta	*Sphagnum sp.*
Ponderosa pine	vascular	Coniferophyta	*Pinus ponderosa*
Prickly pear cactus	vascular	Anthophyta	*Opuntia humifusa*
Purple coneflower	vascular	Anthophyta	*Echinacea purpurea*
Western bracken fern	vascular	Pterophyta	*Pteridium aquilinum*
White willow	vascular	Anthophyta	*Salix alba L.*

Concept Mapping

Page 12 • Classification of Plants

1. nonvascular plants
2. vascular plants
3. bryophytes
4. seeds
5. mosses
6. liverworts
7. cones
8. conifers

9. seeds

10. anthophytes

11. horsetails *or* ferns

12. ferns *or* horsetails

Study Guide

Page 13 • Section 21.1

1. Green Algae, Plants
2. Plants
3. Green Algae, Plants
4. Green Algae, Plants
5. Plants
6. Plants
7. Green Algae, Plants

Note: Student responses for questions 8–12 are interchangeable.

8. a fatty coating called the cuticle on the outer surface of their cells
9. stomata to enable the exchange of gases
10. vascular tissue to move and transport substances through the tissues
11. spores for reproduction
12. a seed structure, covered with a protective coat, that contains an embryo and nutrients for the embryo
13. haploid
14. diploid
15. gametophyte
16. sporophyte
17. dominant
18. spores

Page 14 • Section 21.2

1. Bryophyta
2. Hepaticophyta
3. multicellular rhizoids
4. unicellular rhizoids
5. leaves
6. climates
7. primitive
8. thallose

Page 15 • Section 21.3

1. Lycophyta, Pterophyta
2. Lycophyta
3. Pterophyta
4. Lycophyta, Pterophyta
5. Pterophyta
6. Pterophyta
7. Lycophyta
8. true
9. in wet and dry areas
10. true
11. sporophyte
12. true
13. gametophytes
14. true

Page 16 • Section 21.4

1. cycads; gymnosperms with cones containing male or female reproductive structures; male and female cones grow on separate plants; large divided leaves like palm trees; natural habitats are tropics and subtropics
2. tropical trees and climbing vines, *Welwitschia;* gymnosperms; live 1500–2000 years; source for ephedrine; live in diverse environments
3. ginkgoes; gymnosperms; one living species; distinctive fan-shaped leaves; male plants produce pollen and female plants produce cones with a fleshy, smelly coating; can thrive in smog-filled and polluted areas
4. shrubs to huge trees; gymnosperms; used for lumber and lumber products; most have male and female cones on different branches of same plant; adapt to many environments; deciduous or evergreen
5. flowering plants; angiosperms; most widely distributed plants; eudicots or dicots based on structure of pollen; annual, biennial, or perennial

Guía de estudio

Página 17 • Sección 21.1

1. Alga verde, Plantas
2. Plantas

3. Alga verde, Plantas

4. Alga verde, Plantas

5. Plantas

6. Plantas

7. Alga verde, Plantas

Nota: Las respuestas de los estudiantes a las preguntas 8–12 son intercambiables.

8. una cubierta grasa llamada cutícula en la superficie exterior de las células

9. estomata para permitir el intercambio de gases

10. tejido vascular para mover y transportar substancias a través de los tejidos

11. esporas para la reproducción

12. una estructura de semilla, cubierta con una capa protectora, que contiene un embrión y nutrientes para el embrión

13. haploides

14. diploides

15. gametofito

16. esporofito

17. dominante

18. esporas

Página 18 • Sección 21.2

1. Bryophyta

2. Hepaticopsida

3. rizoides multicelulares

4. rizoides unicelulares

5. hojas

6. climas

7. primitivas

8. talosas

Página 19 • Sección 21.3

1. Licofitas, Terofitas

2. Licofitas

3. Terofitas

4. Licofitas, Terofitas

5. Terofitas

6. Terofitas

7. Licofitas

8. verdadero

9. en áreas húmedas y secas

10. verdadero

11. esporofito

12. verdadero

13. gametofitos

14. verdadero

Página 20 • Sección 21.4

1. cícadas; gimnospermas con conos que contienen estructuras reproductivas masculina o femenina; los conos masculinos y femeninos crecen en plantas separadas; hojas grandes divididas como palmeras; sus hábitats naturales son los trópicos y subtrópicos

2. árboles tropicales y enredaderas, la *Welwitschia*; gimnospermas; viven 1500–2000 años; fuente de la efedrina; viven en ambientes diversos

3. ginkgos; gimnospermas; una especie viviente; hojas diferenciadas en forma de abanico; las plantas masculinas producen polen y las plantas femeninas producen conos con una capa carnosa y maloliente; pueden sobrevivir en áreas contaminadas y en presencia de smog.

4. desde arbustos hasta árboles inmensos; gimnospermas; se usan para madera y productos derivados; la mayoría tiene conos masculinos y femeninos en diferentes ramas de la misma planta; se adaptan a muchos ambientes; temporales o siempre verdes

5. plantas con flores; angiospermas; plantas más ampliamente distribuidas; eudicotiledóneas o dicotiledóneas con base en la estructuras de polen; anuales, bienales, o perennes

Section Quick Check

Page 21 • Section 21.1

1. The two plant groups are vascular plants and nonvascular plants.

2. They both have cell walls made of cellulose, have cell division that includes the formation of cell plates, and use the same type of chlorophyll in photosynthesis. They share similar genes for ribosomal RNA. Food is stored as starch in both. They have the same types of enzymes in cellular vesicles.

3. Vascular tissue allows faster transport. This means substances can be quickly moved from one end of a plant to the other end. If the plant is large, transport would be too slow without vascular tissue.

4. This plant is a seedless vascular plant. It has a specialized transport system, which is vascular tissue. It reproduces with spores and does not have seeds.

5. Desert plants have thick cuticles to help prevent the evaporation of water from plant tissues and to reduce water loss.

Page 22 • Section 21.2

1. The divisions are Bryophyta (mosses), Anthocerophyta (hornworts), and Hepaticophyta (liverworts).

2. Mucilage provides a place for cyanobacteria to grow. Hornworts and cyanobacteria exhibit mutualism.

3. Liverworts and mosses tend to grow in moist areas, and water and nutrients are transported by osmosis and diffusion. They both have leaf-like structures. Liverworts have unicellular rhizoids. Mosses have multicellular rhizoids.

4. Mosses are most like vascular plants because they can have leaflike structures, stems, multicellular rootlike rhizoids, and some tissues to transport food and water.

5. Liverworts tend to grow close to the ground and in moist areas because they lack vascular tissue. Growing close to the ground and in moist areas allows water to be transported throughout them by osmosis and diffusion.

Page 23 • Section 21.3

1. An epiphyte is a plant that lives anchored to an object or another plant.

2. The fern gametophyte might or might not use fertilization to produce a sporophyte. In the leafy structure of the sporophyte, fern spores form in a sporangium. The spores grow to form the gametophyte.

3. Horsetails and lycophytes both produce spores in strobili at the tips of reproductive stems.

4. Rhizomes are food-storage organs. The fern's aboveground structures die during winter and cannot produce food. When warm weather returns in the spring, the rhizome's food is broken down for growth to resume.

5. Fertilization would be difficult in dry areas because it requires a liquid medium, usually water, for the sperm to swim to the eggs.

Page 24 • Section 21.4

1. Conifers can be low-growing shrubs or towering trees. Most have reproductive structures that develop in cones, they have a waxlike coating called cutin, and they have needlelike or scalelike leaves.

2. *Gymnosperm* means naked seed. The seeds of gymnosperms are not part of a fruit.

3. Evergreens are defined as plants with some green leaves throughout the year. In northern temperate regions, most evergreens are conifers. In tropical climates, other plants also maintain their leaves year round. Deciduous trees lose their leaves at the end of a growing season. Some conifers are deciduous.

4. The plant is a perennial angiosperm. It is an angiosperm because it produces flowers and a perennial because it drops its leaves in the winter and resumes growth in the spring.

5. *Welwitschia* lives in the desert. Its leaves can absorb water from fog, dew, or rain, which increases the plant's access to water when there is none for the root to absorb from the ground.

Chapter Test A

Page 25 • Part A: Multiple Choice

1. A
2. A
3. C

Page 25 • Part B: Matching

1. B
2. A
3. C

Page 25 • Part C: Interpreting Diagrams and Charts

1. A: nutrients; B: seed coat; C: embryo
2. A: seedless vascular plants; B: gymnosperms; C: angiosperms
3. From the chart, gymnosperms would appear in the fossil record before angiosperms.

Page 26 • Part D: Short Answer

1. Vascular tissues quickly transport food and water over large distances throughout the plant. Plants with vascular tissues can grow farther away from an aquatic environment. The tissues also provide structure and support for the plant, enabling it to grow larger. Larger plants can root themselves into soil and are more difficult to knock down.
2. Annuals live for one growing season. Biennials live for two years. Perennials can live for several years.

Page 27 • Part E: Concept Application

1. Both cells have a cell wall made of cellulose. As their cells divide, a cell plate forms. Both have similar chlorophyll inside their cells.
2. The primary reproductive structures of a white pine tree are cones. The tree will have male and female cones. Male cones are smaller and produce pollen. Female cones protect the tree's seeds until they mature.

Chapter Test B

Page 28 • Part A: Multiple Choice

1. A
2. C
3. B
4. C
5. D

Page 28 • Part B: Matching and Completion

Matching Set 1

1. B
2. C
3. D
4. E

Matching Set 2

5. C
6. D
7. A
8. B

Completion

9. stoma
10. vascular tissues
11. liverwort

Page 29 • Part C: Interpreting Diagrams and Charts

1. A: nutrients; B: seed coat; C: embryo. The embryo (C) will develop into a new plant.
2. A: nonvascular plants; B: seedless vascular plants; C: gymnosperms; D: angiosperms
3. The fossil record indicates the appearance of seed-bearing gymnosperms before flower-producing angiosperms.

Page 30 • Part D: Short Answer

1. The plant's tissues would suffer from excessive water loss due to evaporation, and the plant's tissues would be susceptible to infection from microscopic pathogens. The plant's leaves could also become dried out because heat is not being reflected away by the cuticle.
2. The triangular shape and drooping branches of the spruce trees enable them to shed excess snow to prevent their branches from breaking. The wax-like coating, called cutin, that covers the spruce's leaves reduces water loss during the dry winter months.

Page 30 • Part E: Concept Application

1. Both organisms have cell walls composed of cellulose, similar ribosomal RNA genes, and the same types of enzymes in their cellular vesicles. Both *Spirogyra* green algae and rosebushes form a cell plate during cell division, photosynthesize with similar chlorophyll, and store food as starch.
2. The *ginkgo biloba* tree would resist the air pollution created by the heavy traffic. Male trees of the species would be preferable because the female trees produce a foul-smelling cone that might make sitting beneath the trees unpleasant.

Chapter Test C

Page 31 • Part A: Multiple Choice

1. C
2. B
3. B
4. A
5. A
6. D

Page 31 • Part B: Completion

1. Pterophyta
2. peat
3. gametophyte
4. Lycophyta
5. Pterophyta
6. cotyledon

Page 32 • Part C: Interpreting Diagrams and Charts

1. A: nutrients; B: seed coat; C: embryo. The seed coat protects the developing embryo from harsh environmental conditions.

2. A: algae; B: nonvascular plants; C: seedless vascular plants; D: gymnosperms; E: angiosperms. Seeds provided developing embryos with a source of food and a protective coating that helped to prevent desiccation. This allowed seeds to survive in habitats that might have previously been a hazard.

3. The development of vascular tissues enabled plants to grow larger and survive farther away from an aquatic environment. Vascular tissues eventually led to the appearance of trees, and forests of trees provided resources for diverse terrestrial ecosystems.

Page 33 • Part D: Short Answer

1. Plants are mulitcellular eukaryotes. They have specialized tissues and organs for performing specific functions. Most plants have photosynthesizing tissues, and most have organs for anchoring them into the ground.

2. A fatty coating, called a cuticle, on the outer surface of aboveground plant cells reduces tissue water loss by evaporation. Pores in the cuticle, called stomata, allow for an exchange of gases in and out of the plant. Vascular tissues quickly transport water, food, and other nutrients over great distances throughout the plant, and they support the plant's body. Using seeds as a reproductive structure, plant embryos can survive dry, harsh environmental conditions.

Page 33 • Part E: Concept Application

1. Kingdom Plantae is divided into major groups called divisions. There are three divisions of nonvascular plants, including Division Bryophyta that classifies mosses, a common deciduous forest plant. There are two divisions of seedless, vascular plants, including Division Pterophyta that classifies all fern species, another common deciduous forest plant. Seed-producing, vascular plants are divided into five divisions. Deciduous trees are classified into Division Anthophyta, and the scattered conifer trees growing in the forest are classified in Division Coniferophyta.

2. The keys of the maple trees aid in the dispersal of their seeds. If the keys are destroyed, the maple seeds will not be scattered away from parent trees. This would cause greater competition between parent trees and their offspring possibly causing a reduction in the Norway maple population.

3. Conifer leaves are small and have a wax-like coating designed to prevent water loss, but in moist, tropical regions, small conifer leaves cannot compete with the broad leaves of tropical trees for sunlight. Conifer trees also have a triangular shape and drooping branches for shedding excess snow, but these characteristics put them at a competitive disadvantage against tall tropical trees that spread their branches upward toward sunlight.

Diagnostic Test

Page 41

1. The correct answer is A. Based on student responses, use the list below to address preconceptions.

- **Student thinks stems are hollow so that water can flow through them.** Introduce student to the role of vascular tissues for transporting water and other materials. Direct student to the discussion of vascular tissues in Section 22.1.

- **Student thinks roots absorb only water.** Direct student to the introductory discussion about roots in Section 22.2.

- **Student thinks roots make food.** Remind student that only structures containing chloroplasts can manufacture food, and these structures are generally green in color. Direct student to the discussion about roots in Section 22.2.

- **Student thinks leaves collect water.** Explain that only plant roots absorb water, and direct student to the discussions about roots and leaves in Section 22.2.

- **Student thinks leaves collect food.** Direct student to the discussion about leaves in Section 22.2.

2. The correct answer is D. Based on student responses, use the list below to address preconceptions.

- **Student thinks the leaf arrangement of trees is the same.** Direct student to the discussion on the characteristics of leaves in Section 22.2.

- **Student thinks all leaves have the same texture.** Direct student to the discussion on the characteristics of leaves in Section 22.2.

- **Student thinks all leaves have the same color.** Explain that most leaves are green in color, but the shade of green among tree leaves varies significantly. Leaves of some trees, such as the Japanese maple tree, also have colors other than green.

- **Student thinks all leaves have only one blade.** Introduce the concept of compound leaves, and direct student to the discussion on the characteristics of leaves in Section 22.2.

- **Student does not think leaves have veins.** Explain that leaves have veins for transporting materials. Direct student to the discussion on the characteristics of leaves in Section 22.2.

- **Student thinks all leaf veins are the same.** Introduce the two major venation patterns, netted and parallel, and direct student to the discussion on the characteristics of leaves in Section 22.2.

3. The loss of a forest would have a potentially drastic impact on a region. Without root systems to hold soil in place, soil erosion will increase. The organisms that depend on trees and the forest habitat will be displaced. The loss of a forest might also impact the economy. The logging industry and many others depend on forest products like trees, nuts, sap, etc. Also, in some areas, loss of forests could decrease ecotourism. Based on student responses, use the list below to address preconceptions.

- **Student fails to understand how roots prevent soil erosion.** Explain that the complex root systems of trees hold soil into the ground

- **Student thinks water exits leaves as a liquid.** Direct student to the discussion of stomata and transpiration in Section 22.2.

- **Student thinks there will be more water in the deforested region because trees are not absorbing it.** Direct student to the discussion of stomata and transpiration in Section 22.2.

- **Student thinks trees serve no economic importance.** Explain that trees are a major source of lumber and fuel. Trees are used to make paper, and forests draw tourism to an area.

- **Student thinks trees are not a major habitat for organisms.** Explain that trees are the foundational source of habitats for a forest ecosystem. Countless species of plants, invertebrates, vertebrates, fungi, and protists live on various tree parts.

- **Student thinks there will be less oxygen in the a deforested region.** Explain that oxygen produced by photosynthesizing organisms is evenly distributed throughout the atmosphere.

Launch Lab

Page 42 • What structures do plants have?

Analysis

1. Most lists should include: leaves, roots, and stems.

2. Student answers should demonstrate logical connections. For example, leaves have a broad surface area to maximize exposure to sunlight.

3. Student answers will vary. Answers may include: thick leaves for water storage, waterproof coverings on leaves, large roots for water storage. Accept all reasonable answers.

MiniLab

Page 43 • Observe Plant Cells

Analysis

1. Students will observe parenchyma cells were observed on the potato slide, collenchyma cells on the celery slide, and Sclerenchyma cells on the pear slide.

2. The cell types were different because the cells were from different plant structures that have different functions. A potato's primary function is carbohydrate storage, so it is composed of mostly parenchyma cells. The celery stalk's main function is support, so it contains many collenchyma cells. The pear is a fruit that surrounds a seed and contains many sclerenchyma cells that cause the gritty texture of the fruit.

MiniLab

Page 44 • Investigate a Plant Response

Analysis

1. Two different hairs must be stimulated to cause the trap to shut. The trap will reopen in about 12 h.

2. Students might realize that a living insect will continue to move. This movement will stimulate more trigger hairs, causing the trap to close more tightly.

BioLab: Design Your Own

Page 45 • Internet: How do dwarf plants respond to gibberellins?

Analyze and Conclude

1. Gibberellic acid causes plants to grow taller if the plants have gibberellin receptors.

2. The plants do not produce enough gibberellic acid.

3. Sample answer: The plants might not be able to grow tall enough to compete with other plants for sunlight.

4. Student answers may include the following: errors in measurement of the concentration of the gibberellin solutions; drift of spray; mistakes in measurement of height; the sample size was not large enough; and variables of light, watering, temperature, etc., were not well controlled.

Real-World Biology: Analysis

Page 47 • Controlling Weeds

Planning the Activity

This activity should be used after students have studied auxins and other plant hormones in Section 22.3 of the text. It can be used to reinforce the concept of plant hormones and their effects on plants.

Purpose

Students investigate the use of synthetic auxins for controlling weeds.

Career Applications

Plant biologists apply biology and biotechnology to improve crop production and find better and safer ways to control weeds. To do this, they use their knowledge of plant physiology, plant molecular biology, chemistry, and biotechnology.

Plant biologists who focus on herbicides might work in product development for the chemical industry. They also might work for the government or universities and research how herbicides work and how they affect the environment.

Teaching Strategies

- Introduce the activity by asking students "Have you ever had to get rid of weeds growing in a garden or lawn?" "Did you pull them out or use

Chapter 22 Teacher Guide and Answers

chemicals?" Encourage students to share what they know about different types of weeds and what makes them easy or hard to kill.

- After students have read the opening paragraphs, have them identify situations in which herbicides could be used.

- Be sure students understand that herbicides need to be used correctly to avoid damaging other plants and harming people, pets, and the environment.

- Have interested students find out more about how herbicides based on synthetic plant hormones are used in agriculture or other industries.

- Below Level: Draw a Venn diagram with two overlapping circles to help students understand how plant hormones and herbicides are related. Label the left circle *plant hormones* and the right circle *herbicides*. Label the overlapping area *auxin-based herbicides*.

- Above Level: Have advanced students design experiments to test the effects of herbicides on various plants. If possible, have them carry out the experiments. Be sure to follow any safety instructions included with the herbicides.

Answers to the Student Worksheet

Analyze and Conclude

1. The bean plant died. The corn plant was not affected.

2. Without a control to compare the results to, there could be other explanations for why the bean plant died, such as that it didn't have enough space to grow in the container.

3. 2,4-D kills eudicots but not monocots.

4. Student answers could include pulling the dandelions by hand or using a herbicide that kills eudicots but not monocots.

5. Corn is a monocot, and tomatoes are eudicots. You would not be able to control weeds by using a herbicide that kills either monocots or eudicots.

Careers in Biology

Plant biologists apply biology and biotechnology to improve crop production and find better and safer ways to control weeds.

Enrichment

Page 49 • Studying Plants for New Compounds

More than a hundred compounds extracted from plants have been found to be effective as medicines or insecticides. In some cases, the discovery of those compounds has proved to be a dramatic story of the isolation of a natural product with significant medical or agricultural benefit. The table provided in the student activity lists only a small fraction of the plant-derived products that can be studied. The last entry in the table provides students with an opportunity to find another compound in which they might be more interested. The purpose of the final assignment—a proposal to the National Science Foundation—provides students not only with an opportunity to summarize the results of their research, but also with a chance to consider the ways in which research funds can best be spent on the development of new chemical products. You might also wish to tie this activity to the issue of maintaining biodiversity in the plant world, assuring that plants that might have important compounds of value to humans will not be lost through extinction.

Concept Mapping

Page 50 • The Structure of Plants

1. roots
2. stems
3. leaves
4. water
5. provide support
6. photosynthesis
7. sclerenchyma cells
8. minerals
9. food
10. xylem

Study Guide

Page 51 • Section 22.1

1. chloroplast
2. cell wall
3. nucleus
4. central vacuole

5. plasma membrane
6. A
7. C
8. B
9. C
10. D
11. D
12. B
13. cork cambium
14. Apical meristems
15. intercalary meristems
16. vascular cambium
17. ground tissue
18. dermal tissue
19. true
20. Trichomes
21. true
22. phloem
23. ground

Page 53 • Section 22.2

1. epidermis
2. endodermis
3. phloem
4. xylem
5. cortex
6. root hair
7. B
8. C
9. A
10. D
11. palisade mesophyll
12. vascular bundle
13. spongy mesophyll
14. blade
15. petiole
16. stoma

Page 54 • Section 22.3

1. Auxin
2. Ethylene
3. Gibberellin

4. Cytokinin
5. Auxin, Gibberellin
6. Ethylene
7. Auxin
8. Gibberellin
9. nastic response
10. positive tropism
11. thigmotropism
12. phototropism
13. negative tropism
14. tropism
15. Solar tracking
16. gravitropism

Guía de estudio

Página 51 • Sección 22.1

1. cloroplasto
2. pared celular
3. núcleo
4. vacuola central
5. membrana plasmática
6. A
7. C
8. B
9. D
10. B
11. D
12. A
13. cambium del corcho
14. meristemas apicales
15. meristemas intercalares
16. cambium vascular
17. tejido fundamental
18. tejido dérmico
19. verdadero
20. Los tricomas
21. verdadero
22. floema
23. fundamental

Página 53 • Sección 22.2

1. epidermis
2. endodermis
3. floema
4. xilema
5. córtex
6. raicilla
7. B
8. C
9. A
10. D
11. mesófilo en empalizada
12. bulto vascular
13. mesófilo esponjoso
14. lámina
15. petiolo
16. estoma

Página 54 • Sección 22.3

1. Auxina
2. Etileno
3. Giberelina
4. Citoquinina
5. Auxina, Giberelina
6. Etileno
7. Auxina
8. Giberelina
9. respuesta nástica
10. tropismo positivo
11. tigmotropismo
12. fototropismo
13. tropismo negativo
14. tropismo
15. seguimiento solar
16. gravitropismo

Section Quick Check

Page 59 • Section 22.1

1. Photosynthesis takes place in ground tissue.

2. Unlike collenchyma and parenchyma cells, sclerenchyma cells lack cytoplasm and other living components when they mature.

3. Three specialized structures of the plant epidermis include stomata, trichomes, and root hairs. Stomata are pores formed by guard cells in the epidermis of leaves and stems. They allow gas exchange. Trichomes are hairlike projections of epidermal cells on stems and leaves. They function in the defense and cooling of a plant. Root hairs are extensions of the epidermis that covers the root tips. They increase the surface area for absorption of water and minerals.

4. Both vessel elements and sieve-tube members are tubular conducting cells in plant vascular tissue. Both are arranged end-to-end in long tubes. Vessel elements are the large conducting cells in the xylem. They lack cytoplasm at maturity, which allows water to flow freely through the xylem vessels. Sieve-tube members are the tubular conducting cells that make up the sieve tubes in phloem. They retain their cytoplasm at maturity, and they conduct dissolved organic and inorganic nutrients throughout a plant.

5. The conducting cells in the vascular tissues, xylem and phloem, carry water and nutrients throughout a plant. Damage to the vascular tissues of a plant could cause all or part of a plant to die if there is no flow of water or nutrients to it.

Page 60 • Section 22.2

1. Roots anchor plants and absorb water and dissolved minerals.

2. An epidermal layer covers a root. Underneath is a cortex made up of the endodermis and the pericycle. The center of a root is made of vascular tissue.

3. Stems grow in length by the addition of cells produced by the apical meristem. Stems can grow in diameter by increasing cell size or by producing new cells in the vascular cambium.

4. Most leaves have a blade that has a relatively large surface area. The tightly packed layer of cells directly below the leaf's upper epidermis, the palisade mesophyll, has maximum exposure to light, and these cells contain many chloroplasts. Below them, the spongy mesophyll cells

are loosely packed to allow the movement of oxygen, carbon dioxide, and water vapor in and out of stomata in the epidermis.

5. A crop that is planted to control erosion should have a fibrous root system. The numerous branching roots of a fibrous root system would be better able to hold the soil in place.

Page 61 • Section 22.3

1. Nastic responses are independent of the direction of the stimulus, are reversible, and can be repeated many times.

2. Because it is a gas, ethylene can diffuse through the spaces between cells.

3. Gibberellins would be the best plant hormone to use in experiments to cause a dwarf plant to grow taller. This is because a lack of genes for gibberellin production has been identified as a cause of dwarfism in some plants.

4. Cytokinins promote cell division by stimulating production of necessary proteins, while auxins promote cell elongation of cells that are already there.

5. Phototropism is a positive tropic response because the plant grows toward the stimulus, the light source.

Chapter Test A

Page 62 • Part A: Multiple Choice

1. A
2. C
3. A

Page 62 • Part B: Matching

Matching Set 1

1. A
2. C
3. B

Matching Set 2

4. A
5. C
6. B

Page 63 • Part C: Interpreting Drawings

1. A: epidermis; B: endodermis; C: phloem; D: xylem; E: cortex

2. The sugar maple tree has simple leaves, which means they have one blade per stalk and netlike venation. The shagbark hickory tree has compound leaves, which means it has more than one leaflet per stalk, and the leaves have an opposite arrangement and netlike venation. The horse chestnut tree also has compound leaves and netlike venation, but the leaves have a whorled arrangement.

Page 63 • Part D: Short Answer

1. Stems support the plant's leaves and reproductive structures. Stems also contain vascular tissues, which transport water, sugar, and dissolved substances throughout the plant.

2. All three types of stems grow underground. Tubers generally have a swollen, oval shape; bulbs have a compressed, round shape; and rhizomes are long stems that grow underground in a horizontal direction.

3. During years when large quantities of water are available, the growth ring will be wider than years when less water is available. The wider ring represents more rapid growth.

Page 64 • Part E: Concept Application

1. Trees and other green plants give off water through their leaves during the process of transpiration. Reducing the number of tropical trees in an area also reduces the amount of moisture being put into the air, resulting in a decrease in the annual rainfall.

2. The plants' gravitropism, which is their response to gravity, could change. The tomato plants' roots might not show positive gravitropism, and their stems might not show negative gravitropism.

Chapter Test B

Page 65 • Part A: Multiple Choice

1. B
2. C
3. D

4. A

5. C

Page 65 • Part B: Matching and Completion

Matching

1. D

2. E

3. A

4. C

Completion

5. auxins

6. ethylene

7. cytokins

8. giberellins

Page 66 • Part C: Interpreting Drawings

1. A: epidermis; B: endodermis; C: phloem; D: xylem; E: cortex

2. The sugar maple tree has simple leaves, which means they have one blade per stalk and netlike venation. The shagbark hickory tree has compound leaves, which means it has more than one leaflet per stalk, and the leaves have an opposite arrangement and netlike venation. The horse chestnut tree also has compound leaves and netlike venation, but the leaves have a whorled arrangement.

Page 67 • Part D: Short Answer

1. All three tissues are responsible for plant growth. Apical meristem tissue increases stem and root length and creates primary growth. Intercalary meristem tissue is found in the stems of monocots and increases stem or leaf length. Lateral meristem tissue creates secondary growth and increases root and stem diameter.

2. Water enters the tree through the roots and is transported throughout the tree via xylem tissues and eventually reaches the leaves. Some of the water is used during the process of photosynthesis occurring primarily in the tree's leaves. Excess water evaporates inside the leaves and exits the leaf through small pores called stomata.

3. Poison ivy leaves contain toxic chemicals that cause severe skin irritation to deter organisms from touching the plant. The leaves of

squash plants are covered with tiny hairs that secrete a substance to repel insects and other herbivores.

Page 67 • Part E: Concept Application

1. Without root hairs, the surface area of the plants' root systems will be greatly reduced, and the plants would not be able to take in as much water and dissolved materials.

2. Trees and other green plants give off water through their leaves during the process of transpiration. Reducing the number of tropical trees in an area also reduces the amount of moisture being put into the air, resulting in a decrease in the annual rainfall. Trees also hold soil. A loss of rain forest trees would cause soil erosion, and the soil would pollute streams and rivers.

Chapter Test C

Page 68 • Part A: Multiple Choice

1. A

2. D

3. B

4. C

5. D

6. C

Page 68 • Part B: Completion

1. parenchyma cells

2. sclerenchyma cells

3. intercalary meristem

4. stomata

5. herbaceous

6. petiole

Page 69 • Part C: Interpreting Drawings

1. A: epidermis; B: endodermis; C: phloem; D: xylem; E: cortex

2. Without the epidermis, root hairs would not grow, and the root could not take in water and minerals. Without the cortex, plant substances could not be transported and stored. Without the endodermis, materials entering the vascular tissues could not be regulated. Water could not flow

throughout the root without xylem, and sugar and organic compounds could not be transported without phloem.

3. The sugar maple, pin oak, and cottonwood trees have simple leaves, which means they have one blade per stalk and netlike venation. The shagbark hickory tree has compound leaves, which means it has more than one leaflet per stalk, and the leaves have an opposite arrangement and netlike venation. The horse chestnut tree also has compound leaves and netlike venation, but the leaves have a whorled arrangement.

Page 70 • Part D: Short Answer

1. Being a dicot, an oak tree has two types of meristem tissues—apical and lateral. The apical meristem tissues promote growth at the tips of the tree's stems and roots. The lateral meristem tissues promote the growth of the diameter of the stems and roots. The oak tree would have two types of lateral meristem tissues. Vascular cambium produces xylem and phloem cells, and cork cambium tissue forms the tree's outer bark.

2. Xylem is composed of specialized cells called vessel elements and tracheids. When mature, these cells consist only of cell walls, and without the presence of cytoplasm, water flows freely though the cells. Tracheids are long, cylindrical cells and are less efficient for transporting materials. Vessel elements are tubular cells stacked end-to-end and open at each end allowing for the free flow of water and dissolved materials.

3. The annual production of xylem and phloem in a year creates a growth ring. A tree's age can be estimated by counting the annual growth rings at the base of its trunk.

Page 70 • Part E: Concept Application

1. The loss of all plant parts such roots, stems, and leaves would result in an overall loss of habitat for rain forest organisms. The loss of plant roots would rapidly increase soil erosion in rain forest areas and contribute to the pollution of rivers and streams. The loss of plant leaves and other structures containing chlorophyll would reduce the food production for these ecosystems and decrease atmospheric oxygen production.

Fewer rain forest plant leaves would mean less transpiration, which would reduce the amount of rainfall in rain forest regions.

2. The control plant will not be overly exposed to predation by herbivores. The cactus plant without spines would be defenseless against the predation of herbivores. The botanist might observe herbivores grazing on the cactus without spines more frequently than the plant with spines.

3. The student could observe the entire stem of the plant growing back toward the light coming through the window, or she could observe the stem of the plant bending into an S shape as the stem's top grows back toward the light.

Chapter 23 Teacher Guide and Answers

Diagnostic Test

Page 77

1. The correct answer is B. Based on student responses, use the list below to address preconceptions.

   - **Student thinks all plants grow from seeds.** Direct student to the moss and fern reproduction and life cycle discussions in Section 23.1.
   - **Student thinks plants do not use the process of fertilization.** Direct student to the seed development discussion in Section 23.1.
   - **Student thinks plants do not produce gametes.** Direct student to the seed development discussion in Section 23.1.
   - **Student thinks all plants produce fruits.** Direct student to the discussions about the reproduction and life cycles of moss, ferns, and conifers in Section 23.1.
   - **Student thinks all plants grow from seeds or spores.** Direct student to the vegetative reproduction discussions in Section 23.1.

2. The correct answer is B. Based on student responses, use the list below to address preconceptions.

   - **Student thinks conifers produce only one type of cone.** Direct student to the conifer reproduction and life cycle discussion in Section 23.1.
   - **Student thinks conifers produce flowers.** Direct student to the conifer reproduction and life cycle discussion in Section 23.1.
   - **Student thinks conifers do not produce male and female gametes.** Direct student to the conifer reproduction and life cycle discussion in Section 23.1.
   - **Student thinks conifers do not produce pollen.** Direct student to the conifer reproduction and life cycle discussion in Section 23.1.

3. The basic structures of a flower include a sepal, petal, stamen, filament, anther, pistil, stigma, style, and ovary. Based on student responses, use the list below to address preconceptions.

   - **Student thinks all plants produce flowers.** Direct student to the discussions about the reproduction and life cycles of moss, ferns, and conifers in Section 23.1.

   - **Student confuses the functions of flowers with the functions of other plant structures.** Direct student to the flower organ discussion in Section 23.1.
   - **Student confuses the functions of flower structures.** Direct student to the flower organ discussion in Section 23.1.
   - **Student does not distinguish between male and female flower parts.** Direct student to the flower organ discussion in Section 23.1.

Launch Lab

Page 78 • What are plant reproductive structures?

Analysis

1. All the plants reproduce sexually by producing sperm and egg cells. Other answers will depend on what the student observes.

2. Answers will vary, but pollen containing sperm nuclei land on the top of the female flower structure (stigma) and fertilize egg cells in the bottom portion of the female structure (ovule).

MiniLab

Page 79 • Compare Conifer Cones

Analysis

1. Answers will vary. Cones vary in size, shape (slender versus oval), color, position on the tree branch, type and shape of scales, and how close the scales fit together.

2. Answers will vary.

MiniLab

Page 80 • Compare Flower Structures

Analysis

1. Answers will vary. Students should notice different positioning and numbers of flower organs.

2. Different colors will attract different types of pollinators.

3. Answers will vary, but the size and shape of flowers and their structures are designed to accommodate the size and behaviors of the pollinators that frequent them.

BioLab: Design Your Own

Page 81 • How do monocot and eudicot flowers compare?

Analyze and Conclude

1. Monocots usually have flower petals in multiples of three or six, parallel veins in leaves, vascular bundles scattered throughout their stems, and fibrous (bushy) roots. Eudicots usually have flower petals in multiples of four or five, netted veins in leaves, vascular bundles on the perimeter of their stems, and thick taproots.

2. Answers will vary.

3. Answers will vary. Differences will depend on the flowers used. Students should use their books or reference materials to correct misidentifications.

Real-World Biology: Lab

Page 83 • Variables Affecting Seed Germination

Planning the Activity

Have students complete this activity after they have studied seed germination in Chapter 23 of the text.

Purpose

Students will design and conduct an experiment to test the effect of a variable on seed germination.

Career Applications

An interest in seed germination and growth can lead to a career in the field of agronomy, a branch of agriculture dealing with the production of crops and soil management. The world's major food crops are grown from seeds. Farmers who grow the crops buy their seeds from seed scientists who specialize in seed research and development, testing, and production. Seed specialists, seed analysts, and certified seed growers need a college degree in agronomy, agricultural business, or a related degree. They might work for the commercial seed industry or public agencies.

Materials Tips

Materials plastic cups, potting material, seeds, metric ruler, water, tape, marker

- Peat pots or other containers can be used instead of plastic cups.

- Any available seeds, such as sunflower, zinnia, bean, radish, or cucumber, can be used. Make sure each student uses only one kind of seed.

- Additional materials might be needed, depending on the variables chosen.

- Provide appropriate space, light, and temperature for planted seeds.

- For days during which students are not able to make observations, such as weekends, have students mark an *X* in **Table 1.**

Safety Tips

Make sure students wash their hands after planting the seeds.

Teaching Strategies

Review how to design an experiment. Ask students "What is a control?" "What is a variable?" "What is a hypothesis?"

- Check and approve students' hypotheses, materials, and procedures before they begin their experiments.

- Depending on the type of seeds used and other variables, seeds will probably germinate in 6 to 14 days.

- **Table 1** is for recording the minimum amount of data. Students could keep additional data, such as the heights and appearance of the seedlings.

- Encourage students to record data as they make their observations.

- If the seeds do not germinate, discuss possible reasons for the lack of germination.

- Have students compile the results from their experiments and develop a class list of how different variables affect seed germination.

- Because the seeds will most likely not begin to germinate before day 6 or 7, you could have students begin recording data on day 6 or 7.

- Below Level: If students have trouble designing their experiments, go through the steps of the scientific method on the board. Emphasize the importance of only changing one variable.

- Above Level: Have advanced students design an experiment to test the effect of another variable on seed germination. If time permits, have them conduct the experiment.

Chapter 23 Teacher Guide and Answers

Answers to Student Worksheet

Analyze and Conclude

1. Answers should reflect the data from the student's experiment.

2. Answers should include how the variable affected seed germination and whether the hypothesis was correct.

3. Answers will vary but should include possible reasons why the variable affected germination as it did.

4. Changes could include increasing the number of *control* and *variable* cups to increase the sample size or expanding the variable to include a continuum of variation, such as exposing the seeds to three or more different temperatures.

5. Answers should reflect the data from the student's experiment.

Careers in Biology

Seed scientists specialize in seed research and development, testing, and production.

Enrichment

Page 85 • Plants for Every Use

Answers will vary. A number of references list plants with a host of human applications that have been discovered by ethnobotanists.

Common Name	Scientific Name	Flower Description	Possible Uses of Plant
Rattlesnake master	*Eryngium yuccifolium*	flowers in dense spherical clusters with small white petals	used in Native American rituals and as antidote to rattlesnake and scorpion venom
Jack-in-the-pulpit	*Arisaema triphyllium*	curving hood with green or purplish green erect club or "Jack"	dried roots used for coughs and colds; corms cooked and eaten or ground into flour
Big bluestem	*Andropogon gerardii*	flowers arranged in groups of three on a stalk	used by Native Americans to make tea for stomachache, indigestion, and fever
Sweet alyssum	*Lobularia maritima*	bunches of small white flowers with four petals	ornamental garden plant and ground cover
Maca	*Lepidium meyenii*	small, off-white flowers similar to those of mustard plant	root used as a staple food among Peruvian Indians and is eaten fresh, dried, or ground
Epazote	*Chenopodium ambrosioides*	small, yellow flowers clustered along reddish stems	used by many Mexican, Central American, and South American peoples as a culinary spice and medicinal herb to kill bacteria, amoeba, and parasites and to expel worms

Chapter 23

Teacher Guide and Answers

Concept Mapping

Page 86 • The Plant Life Cycle

1. cell division
2. haploid spores
3. gametophytes
4. haploid gametes
5. eggs
6. fertilization
7. diploid zygote
8. cell division

Study Guide

Page 87 • Section 23.1

1. asexual
2. true
3. true
4. true
5. tissue culture
6. gametophyte; sporophyte
7. diploid
8. egg; sperm
9. nonvascular
10. largest
11. meiosis
12. chemotaxis
13. C
14. E
15. D
16. B
17. A
18. heterosporous
19. microspores
20. micropyle
21. megaspores
22. mature sporophyte
23. male cone
24. female cone

Page 89 • Section 23.2

1. stigma
2. petal
3. ovary
4. ovule
5. anther
6. filament
7. sepal
8. perfect flower
9. monocots
10. What are animal-pollinated flowers like?
11. What happens during self-pollination?
12. short-day
13. long-day
14. day-neutral
15. intermediate-day

Page 90 • Section 23.3

1. E
2. B
3. C
4. A
5. D
6. Dry fruits
7. Aggregate fruits
8. Multiple fruits
9. Simple fleshy fruits
10. seed coat
11. embryo
12. cotyledon
13. hypocotyl
14. radicle
15. first leaves

Guía de estudio

Página 91 • Sección 23.1

1. asexual
2. verdadero
3. verdadero
4. verdadero
5. cultivo de tejido

6. gametofito; esporofito

7. diploides

8. huevo; esperma

9. no vasculares

10. más larga

11. meiosis

12. quimiotaxis

13. C

14. E

15. D

16. B

17. A

18. heterospora

19. microsporas

20. micrófilo

21. megasporas

22. esporofito maduro

23. cono masculino

24. cono femenino

Página 93 • Sección 23.2

1. estigma

2. pétalo

3. ovario

4. óvulo

5. antera

6. filamento

7. sépalo

8. flor perfecta

9. monocotiledóneas

10. ¿Qué son flores polinizadas por animales?

11. ¿Qué pasa durante la autopolinización?

12. día corto

13. día largo

14. día neutro

15. día intermedio

Página 94 • Sección 23.3

1. E

2. B

3. C

4. A

5. D

6. frutos secos

7. frutos agregados

8. frutos múltiples

9. frutos carnosos simples

10. cubierta de la semilla

11. embrión

12. cotiledón

13. hipocotilo

14. radícula

15. primeras hojas

Section Quick Check

Page 95 • Section 23.1

1. The life cycle of a plant includes a diploid sporophyte stage and a haploid gametophyte stage that alternate.

2. A film of water is needed for fertilization in nonvascular plants because the eggs and sperm are produced in separate structures and the sperm must swim to the eggs.

3. The moss sporophyte is small, cannot undergo photosynthesis, and is dependent on the gametophyte for nutrition and support. The fern sporophyte is large and is photosynthetic.

4. The gametophyte generation of a conifer is dependent on the sporophyte generation.

5. Vegetative reproduction will be preferred because it will produce plants exactly like the original. Sexual reproduction can cause a recombination of the genes from two different plants, and the desired characteristic might be lost.

Page 96 • Section 23.2

1. The stamen is composed of the filament, or stalk, and the anther. The filament supports the anther. Inside the anther are cells that form pollen grains.

2. Petals and sepals are the nonreproductive parts of a flower.

3. Such flowers would be wind-pollinated. Flowers that lack showy petals do not attract insects or birds. The huge amounts of pollen increase the success of fertilization when the pollen is dispersed by wind.

4. Exposing a short-day plant to long days will keep the plant from producing flowers.

5. Plants with imperfect flowers are more likely to be cross-pollinated. The reason for this is that pollen must be transported to a different flower for pollination to occur. The different flower is most likely to be on a different plant.

Page 97 • Section 23.3

1. First, the seed absorbs water and swells, which can break the seed coat. Next, digestive enzymes break down stored food. Finally, the radicle appears outside the seed coat, and the hypocotyl appears above the soil.

2. A monocot seed contains endosperm and one small cotyledon. A eudicot seed has no endosperm and two large cotyledons. When germinating, the hypocotyl of some eudicot seeds pulls the cotyledons out of the ground. The cotyledon of a monocot seed usually remains in the soil.

3. Pollination is the transfer of pollen from the anther to the stigma. Fertilization is the fusing of sperm and egg and sperm and polar nuclei. This occurs after pollination and growth of the pollen tube.

4. Both seeds and fruits can aid in dispersal. A seed contains an embryonic sporophyte and a stored food supply. One or more seeds can develop within a single fruit. A seed develops from an ovule, and a fruit develops from the ovary wall and, sometimes, other parts of the flower.

5. Dormancy enables seeds to delay growth until conditions become favorable for plant growth. It helps the embryo in a seed to stay alive in harsh conditions.

Chapter Test A

Page 98 • Part A: Multiple Choice

1. B
2. D
3. A

Page 98 • Part B: Matching

1. C
2. B
3. A

Page 98 • Part C: Interpreting Drawings

1. A: anther; B: petal; C: ovary
2. Seed Type 1: eudicot seed; Seed Type 2: monocot seed
3. The structure is the endosperm, which provides nourishment for the developing embryo.

Page 99 • Part D: Short Answer

1. Female cones contain egg-producing ovules, while male cones produce pollen.
2. Pollination occurs when the pollen grain from one species of seed plant lands on the stigma of a plant of the same species.
3. Without its brightly colored, fragrant petals, the rose plant would not be able to attract pollinators to its reproductive organs, and potential pollinators would have no platform on which to land if they approached the flower.

Page 100 • Part E: Concept Application

1. Many crops could not be grown as quickly. The specific crops grown by farmers would not be as uniform, and there would be less diversity of crops grown by humans.
2. When the seeds absorb water, germination begins. Water transports materials to the growing regions of the seeds. The food stored inside the seeds is converted into energy in the presence of oxygen, and this energy promotes growth in the new plant.

Chapter Test B

Page 101 • Part A: Multiple Choice

1. B
2. C
3. C
4. D
5. D

Page 101 • Part B: Matching and Completion

Matching

1. C
2. B
3. A

Chapter 23 \ *Teacher Guide and Answers*

Completion

4. heterosporous
5. pistil
6. photoperiodism
7. polar nuclei

Page 102 • Part C: Interpreting Drawings

1. A: petal; B: anther; C: filament; D: stigma; E: ovary
2. Seed Type 1: eudicot seed; Seed Type 2: monocot seed
3. A: seed coat; B: embryo; C: cotyledon

Page 103 • Part D: Short Answer

1. Many plants rely on animals to transfer pollen, and they produce flowers with bright colors, strong odors, or sweet nectar to attract animal pollinators. Plants depending on the wind for pollination produce lightweight pollen and lack bright or fragrant flowers. Self-pollinating plants have organs capable of pollinating themselves or other flowers from the same plant.

2. During germination, the seed starts to grow, and it absorbs water. Water transports nutrients to growing parts of the seed. Digestive enzymes break down food, but oxygen is needed for cellular respiration. Without sufficient oxygen supplies, the seed cannot produce energy for growth.

Page 103 • Part E: Concept Application

1. Using vegetative reproduction, young plants have a constant nutrient supply from the parent plant, can develop and grow more quickly, and still reproduce when environmental conditions do not favor seed germination.

2. Scientists can identify the family or genus of a pollen grain by examining the distinctive outer layer of its cell wall. Paleontologists can collect pollen samples from a specific time period of ancient Earth in locations around the globe. They could identify the types of plants living during that time by examining and identifying the pollen grains, and by knowing the plant types that dominated the landscape; scientists could infer climatic conditions for different regions of the planet.

Chapter Test C

Page 104 • Part A: Multiple Choice

1. C
2. D
3. B
4. B
5. A
6. D

Page 104 • Part B: Completion

1. prothallus
2. pistil
3. monocot
4. anthophytes
5. photoperiodism
6. radicle

Page 105 • Part C: Interpreting Drawings

1. A: petal; B: sepal; C: anther; D: filament; E: stigma; F: ovary; G: ovule
2. Seed Type 1: eudicot seed; Seed Type 2: monocot seed
3. Both types of seeds have a seed coat, cotyledon, and developing embryo. The monocot has an endosperm, while the eudicot does not.

Page 106 • Part D: Short Answer

1. Vegetative reproduction is a form of asexual reproduction in which new plants grow from existing plant parts such as roots, leaves, or stems. The new plants are genetic clones of the original plant. Crossbreeding creates seeds from the union of female and male gametes. The new plants inherit half their DNA from each parent.

2. The life cycle of a plant includes a haploid gametophyte stage and a diploid sporophyte stage. The first cell division of the gametophyte stage results in male and female gametes (eggs and sperm). These gametes form a diploid zygote after fertilization, which is the first cell of the sporophyte stage. The first cell division of the sporophyte stage yields reproductive cells, and haploid spores are formed by the process of meiosis.

3. The outer layer of a pollen grain's cell wall, called the exine, can be used to determine the family or genus of the pollen. If paleontologists can determine the types of plants living in a specific time period by examining the exine of their pollen, they can estimate the type of climate the plant types require to thrive.

Page 106 • Part E: Concept Application

1. The student is observing pollination not fertilization. Pollination is the process of pollen from one species of plant landing on the female reproductive organs of another plant of the same species. After pollination, a pollen grain must travel to the ovule, which can take a year or longer, and the pollen forms sperm cells. When egg and sperm join, fertilization occurs, which creates a zygote and eventually a seed.

2. Seeds dispersed by wind often have lightweight, fluffy structures to catch wind currents, and some seeds, such as maple tree keys, have wing shapes to spin through the air. Seeds dispersed by animals are often found in sweet fruits or nutritious nuts that attract the animals to eat them. The indigestible seeds then are excreted from the animal at a location far from the parent plant, or the seeds can be dropped or buried.

3. The seeds of many wild plants require a dormancy stage, which is a time of little or no growth. Some seeds, such as those of the East Indian lotus, can remain dormant for hundreds of years to survive inhospitable environmental conditions. When growing conditions are favorable, the seeds take in water and begin the germination process.